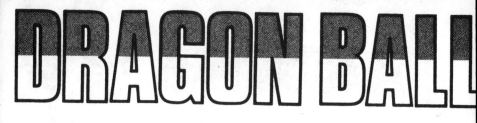

DRAGON BALL

DBZ : 59 • Showdown!

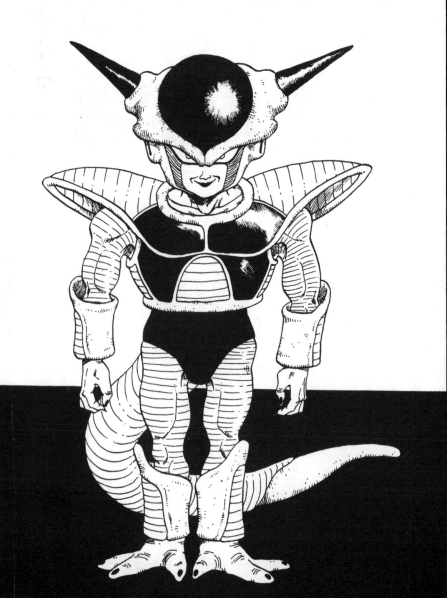

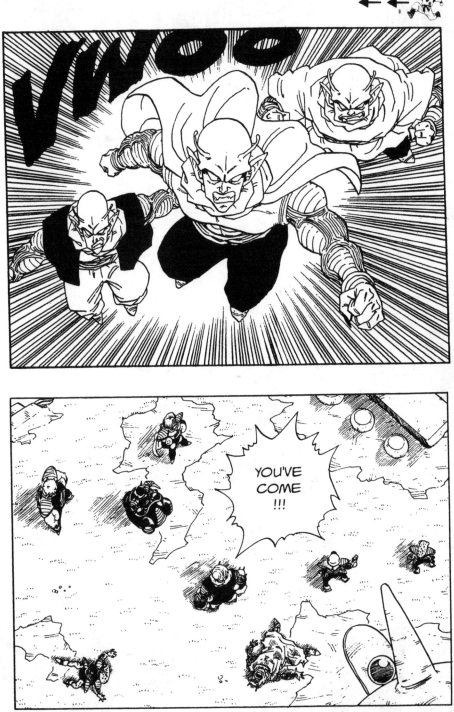

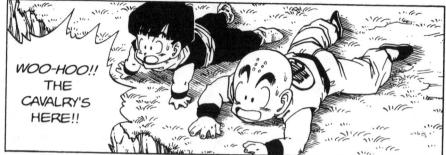

WOO-HOO!!
THE
CAVALRY'S
HERE!!

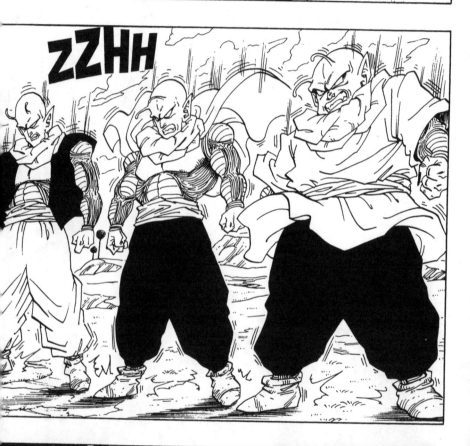

ZZHH

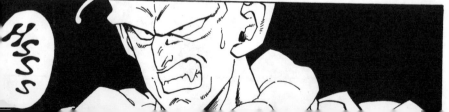

HSSS

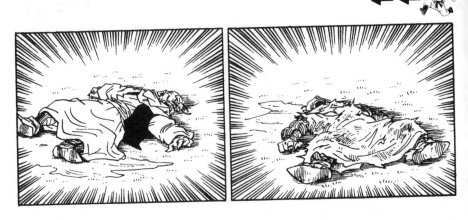

IT IS
AS WE
FEARED...

YOU'VE HAD
TO COME
ALONG...
AND MAKE
US WASTE
OUR TIME
KILLING YOU.

THIS IS SO
ANNOYING.
JUST WHEN
WE'D
PERSUADED
THEM TO GO
GET US THAT
DRAGON
BALL...

...DISRUPTING THE HARD-WON PEACE OF NAMEK!

THEY WILL REGRET...

THE RUMORS OF DRAGON BALL THIEVES RAIDING THE VILLAGES ARE TRUE.

INDEED...

BE CAREFUL, MY BRETHREN... THEIR POWER IS CONSIDERABLE...!

GOOD LUCK!!

piiiii

WHAT SORT OF COMBAT POWER DO THEY HAVE, MR. DODORIA?

OH! YOU PLAN TO FIGHT!

I'LL CHECK, SIR!

!!

NOT EVEN WORTH OUR TROUBLE.

YOU'LL BE DISAPPOINTED, SIR. ALL THREE RATE AT APPROXIMATELY 1000.

HEH HEH HEH...

pip pip

THAT DEVICE READS THE *CHI* OF LIVING THINGS!!

THEN *THAT'S* HOW THEY'VE BEEN ABLE TO FIND THE FEW VILLAGES SCATTERED OVER THE VAST PLANET NAMEK!!

YOU'RE REALLY GOING TO FACE US WITH POWERS OF...WA-HA-HA!... 1000?!

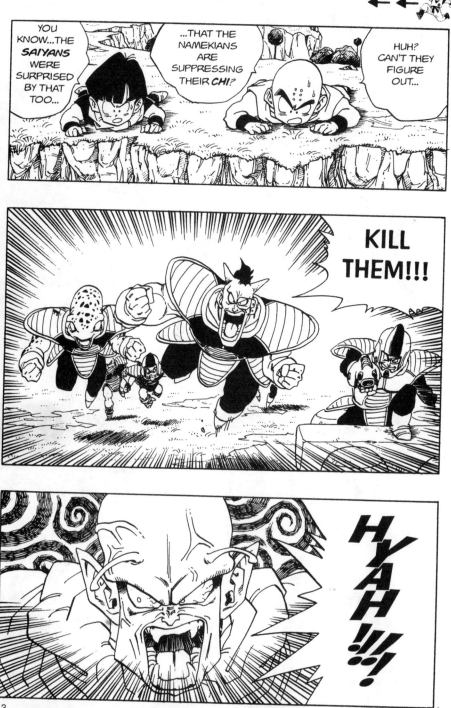

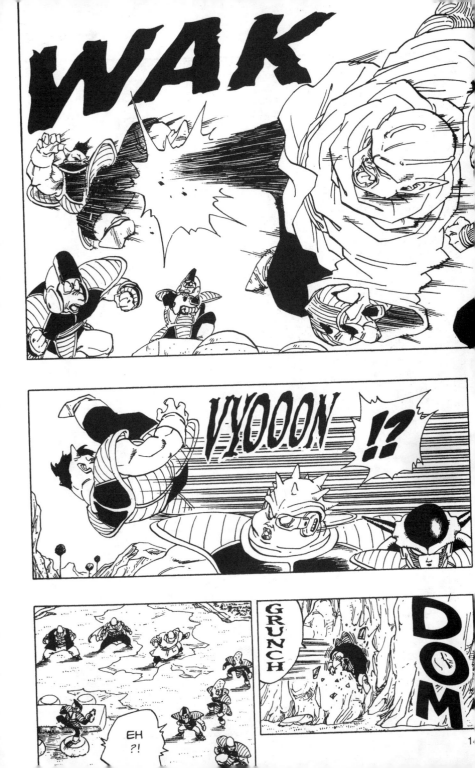

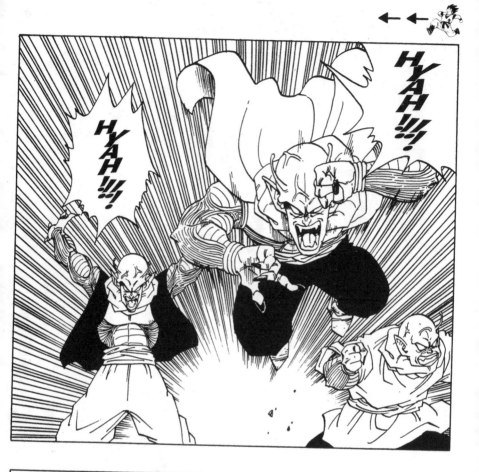

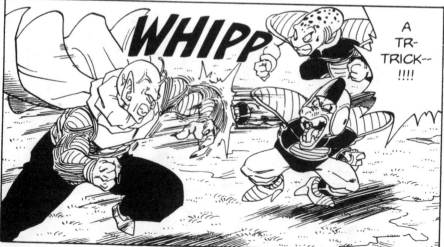

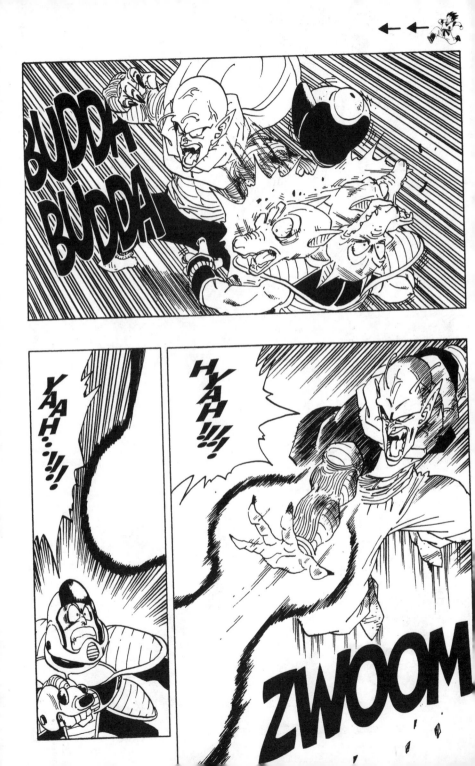

WHAT IS THIS?! THAT'S NO 1000 POWER!!

KCHK KCHK

I...I DON'T UNDERSTAND! THEY'VE ALL INCREASED TO 3000!

BASSHH

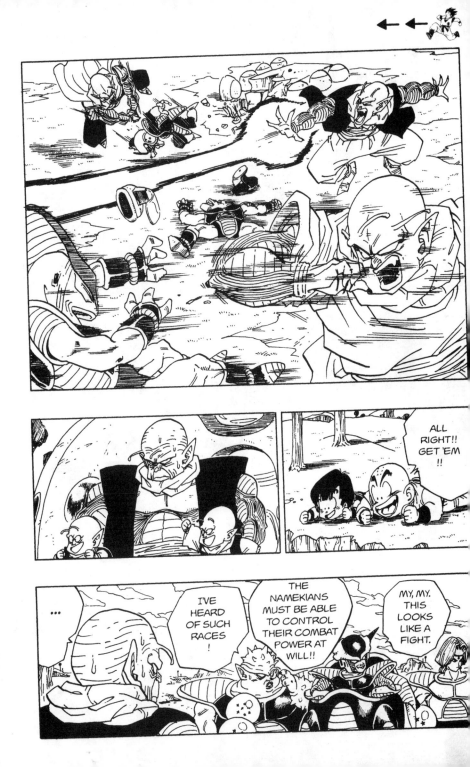

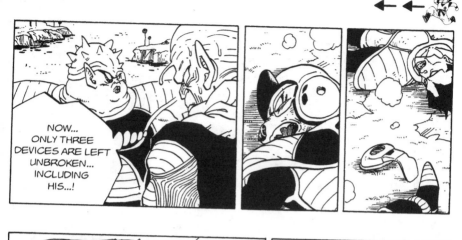

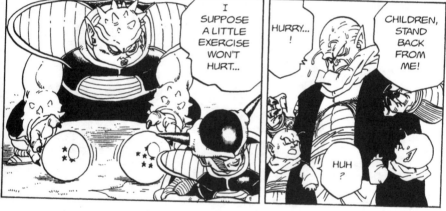

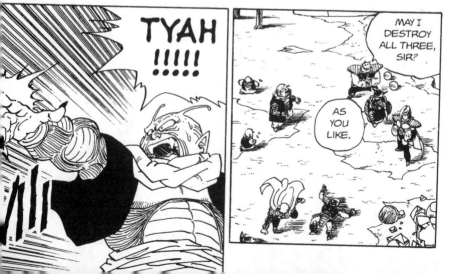

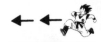
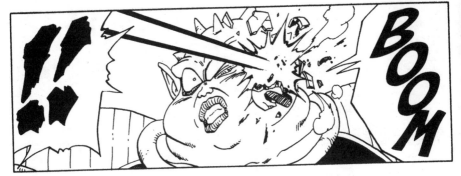

DID YOU THINK *THAT* MOVE...COULD DEFEAT *ME*...?!

FOOL...!!

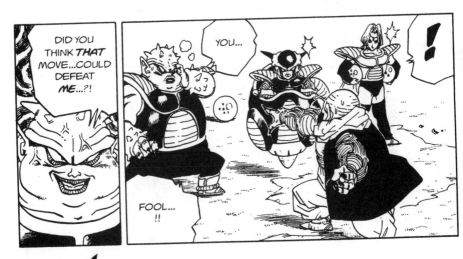

YOU...

!

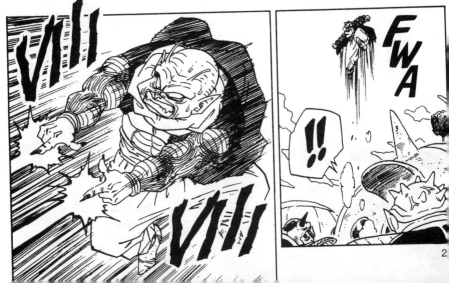

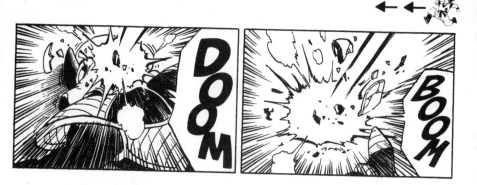

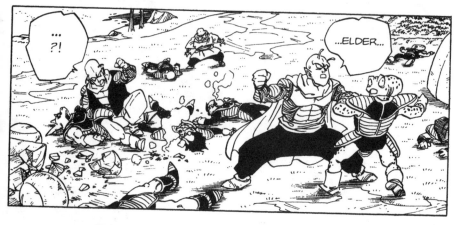

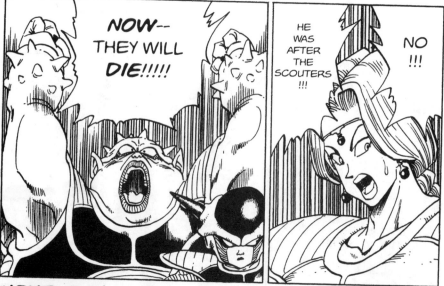

NEXT: *Dodoria Enraged!*

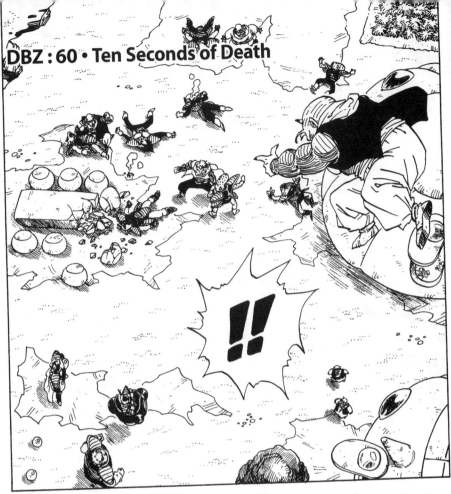

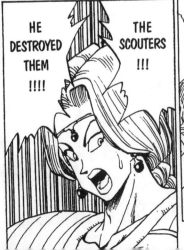

HE DESTROYED THEM !!!!

THE SCOUTERS !!!

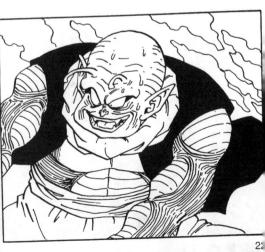

THOSE THINGS THAT TELL 'EM WHERE THEIR ENEMIES ARE AND HOW STRONG THEY ARE!

SCOUTERS... ?!

CURSE THEM !!

THEY USED THOSE GADGETS TO FIND NAMEKIANS-- AND TOOK THE DRAGON BALLS FROM THEM!!

THE OLD NAMEKIAN FIGURED IT OUT-- AND WIPED OUT THE GADGETS!!

I GET IT!! IT WASN'T THAT THEY *KNEW* THE LOCATIONS OF THE DRAGON BALLS!!

I'LL WIPE OUT EVERY SINGLE ONE OF THEM !!!!

I'LL KILL THEM ALL !!!!

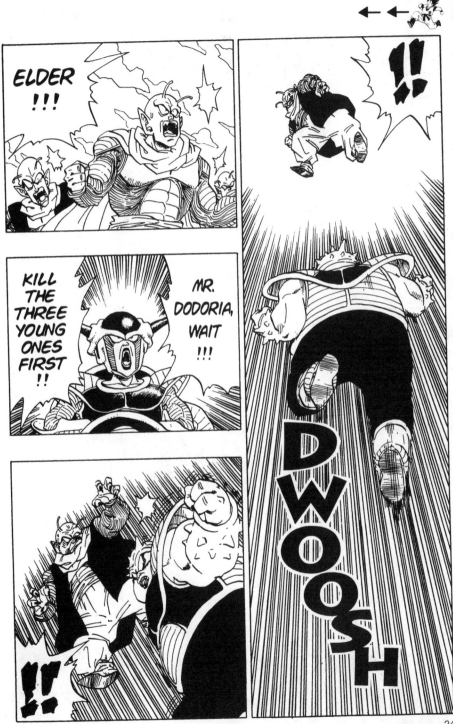

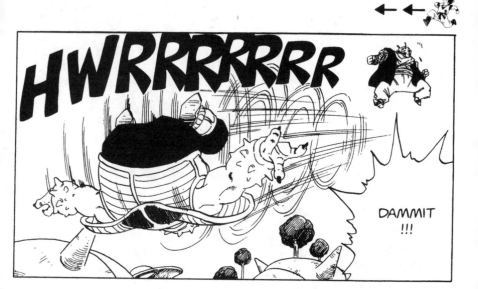

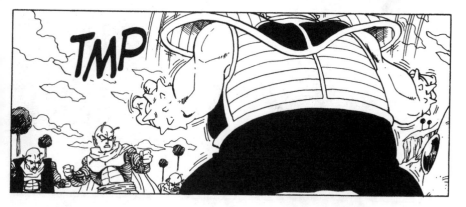

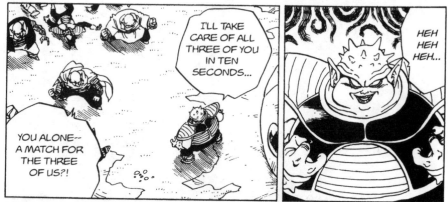

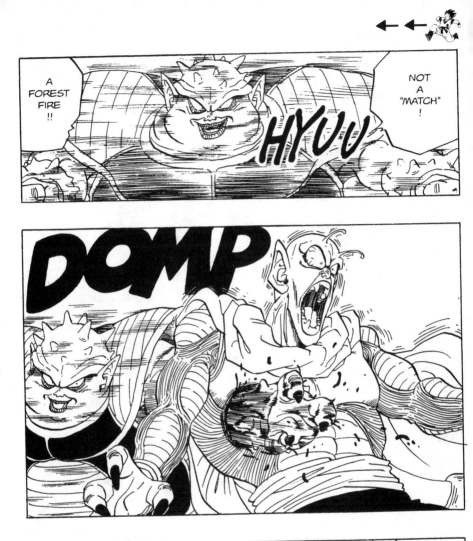

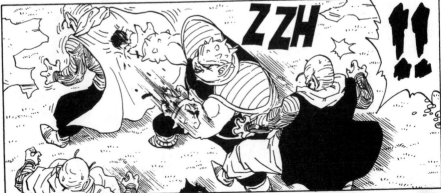

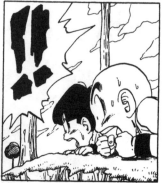

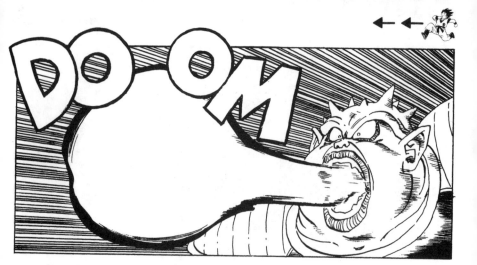

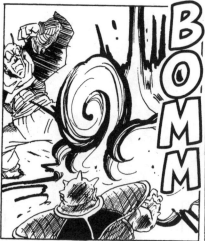

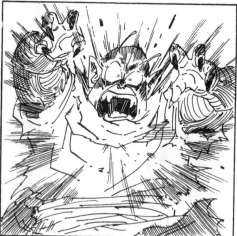

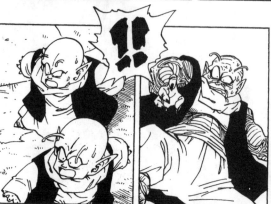

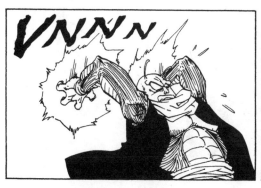

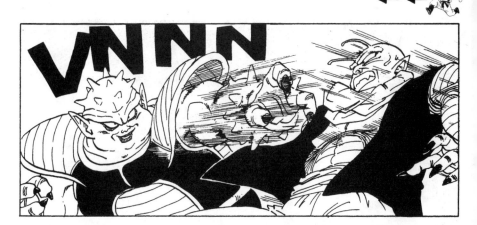

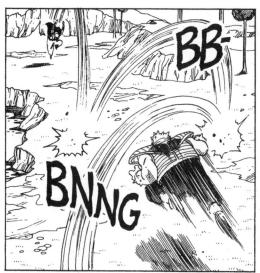

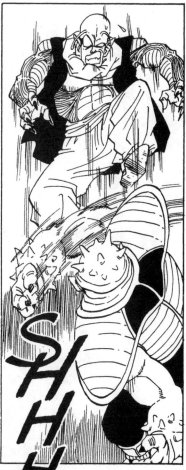

28

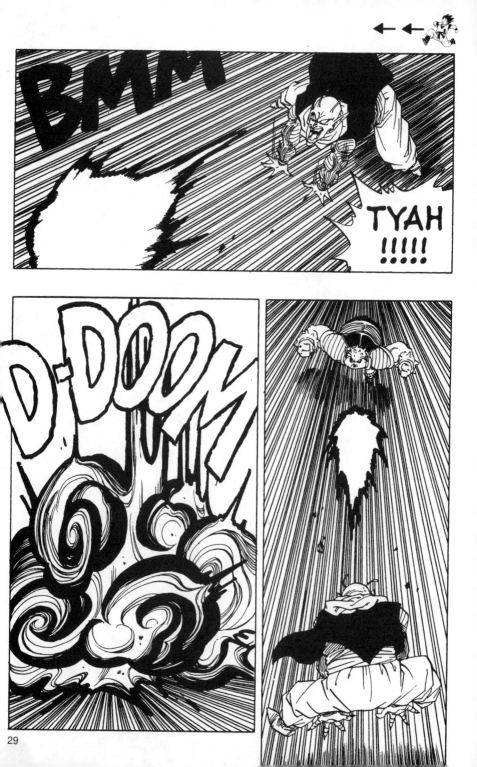

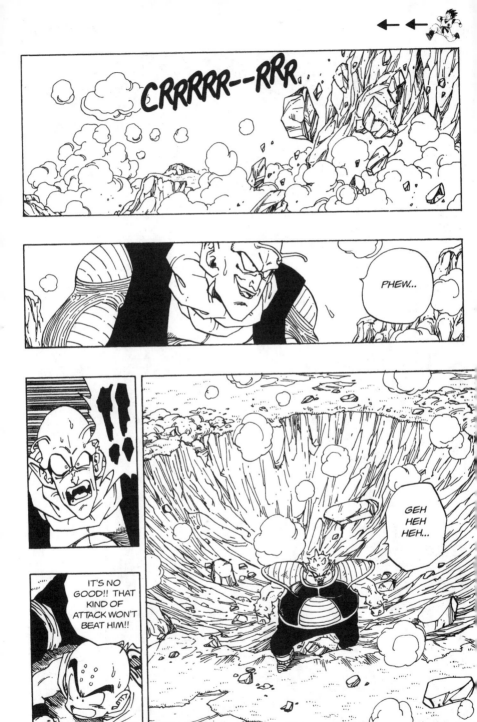

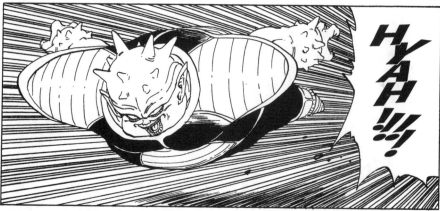

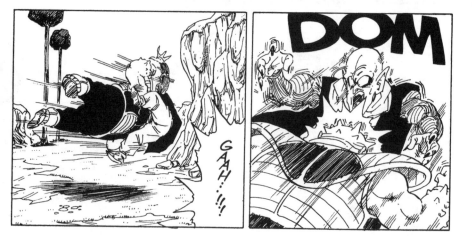

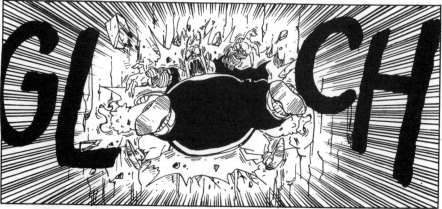

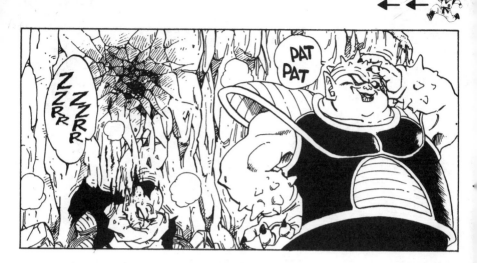

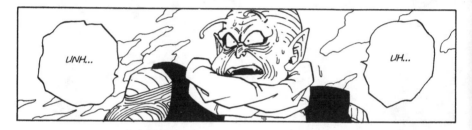

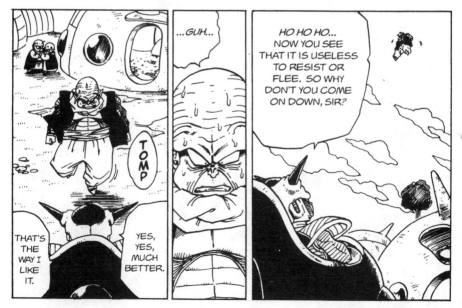

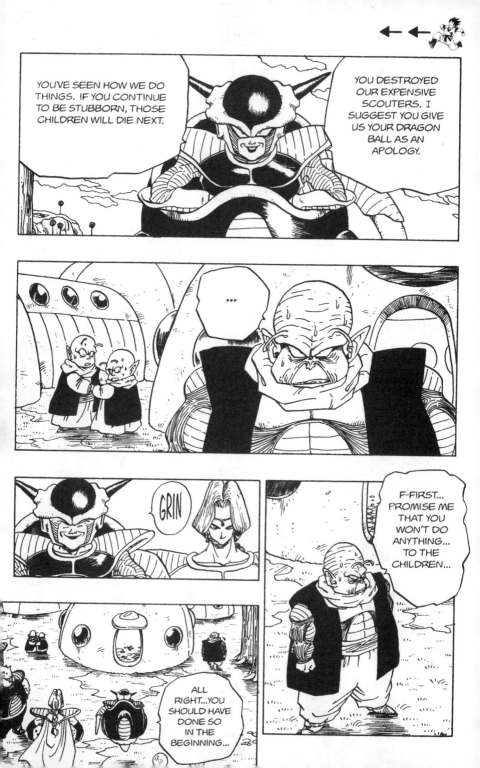

I...I CAN'T BELIEVE THOSE MONSTERS...

TH-THESE ARE *NOT* GUYS WE SHOULD BE GOING UP AGAINST!!

G-GOHAN... WHOA!! DON'T GET ANY CRAZY IDEAS!!

THEY WON'T GET AWAY WITH IT!

THANK YOU.

TAKE THIS... AND GO!

34

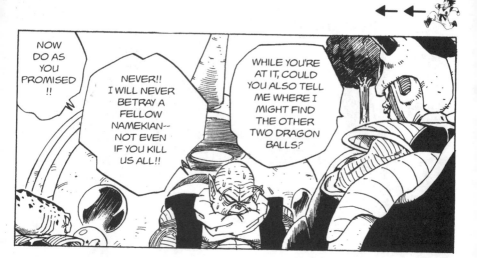

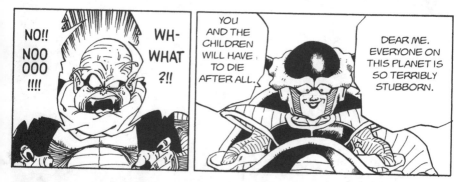

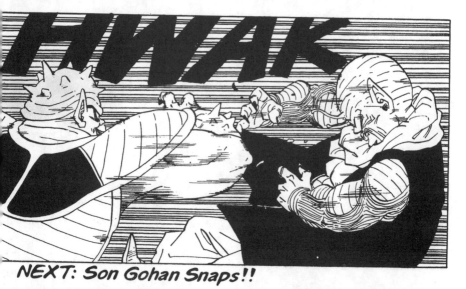

NEXT: *Son Gohan Snaps!!*

YOU... GAVE YOUR *WORD*...!

I GAVE YOU THE DRAGON BALL! NOW LEAVE US IN PEACE!!

WAH !!!

YOU DESTROYED THE SCOUTERS WE USED TO FIND THEM. SO YOU MUST TELL US WHERE THE OTHERS ARE.

BUT THE DRAGON BALLS ARE WORTHLESS UNLESS WE HAVE ALL SEVEN OF THEM, YES ?

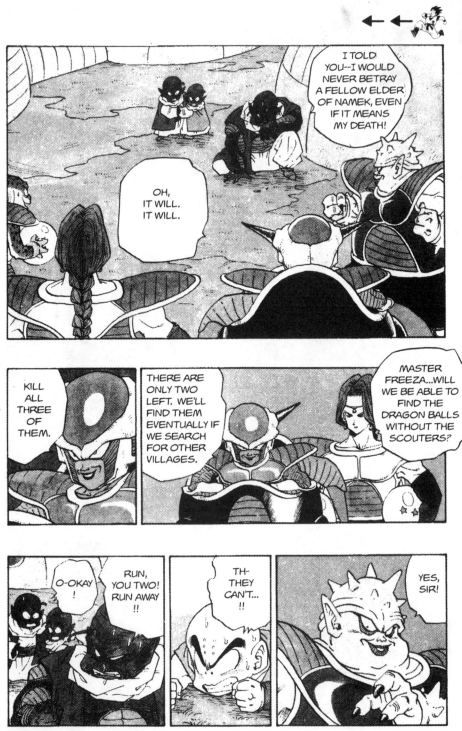

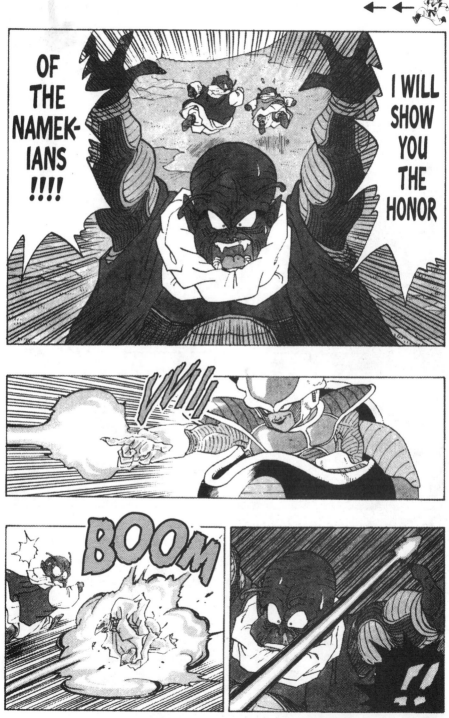

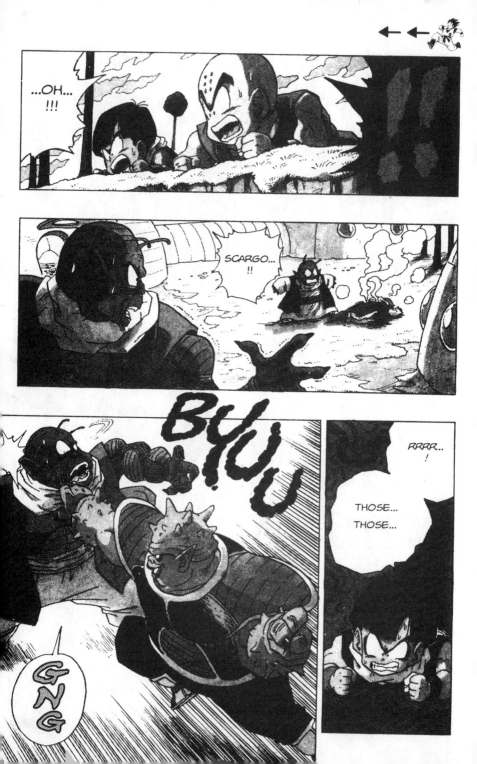

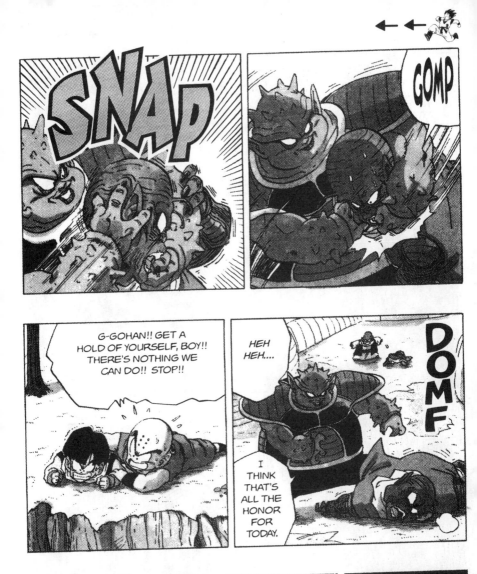

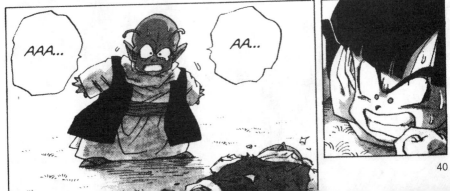

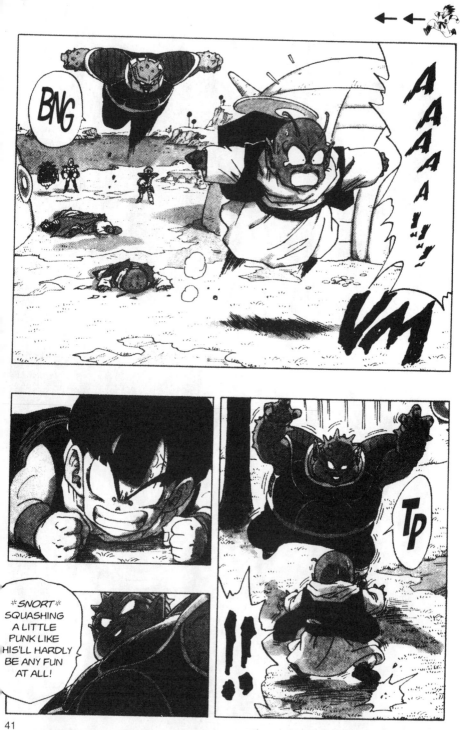

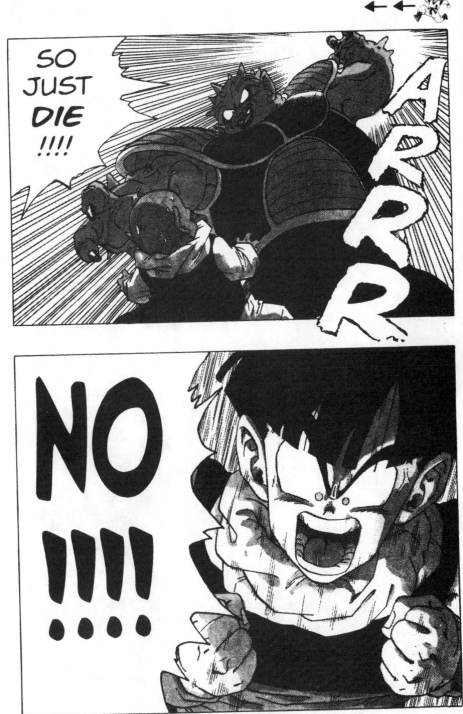

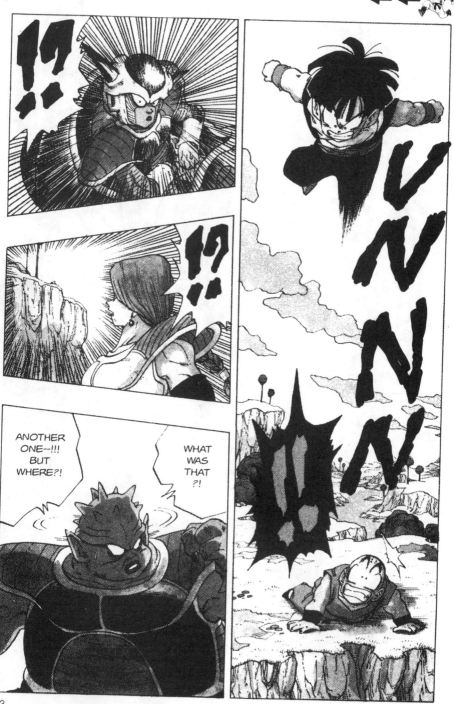

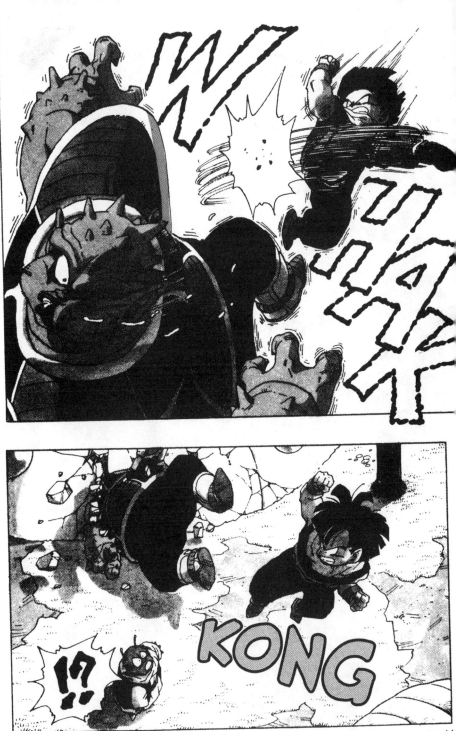

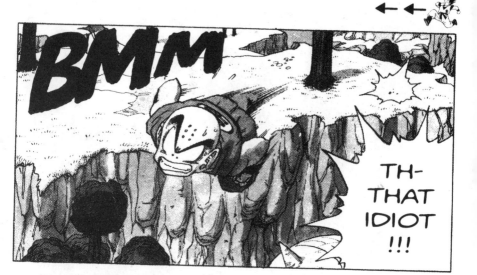

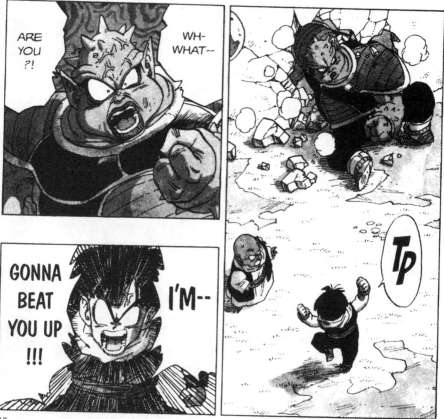

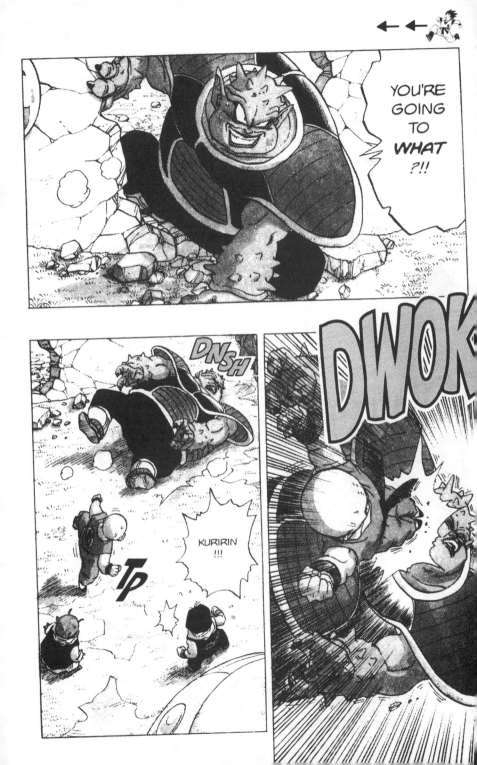

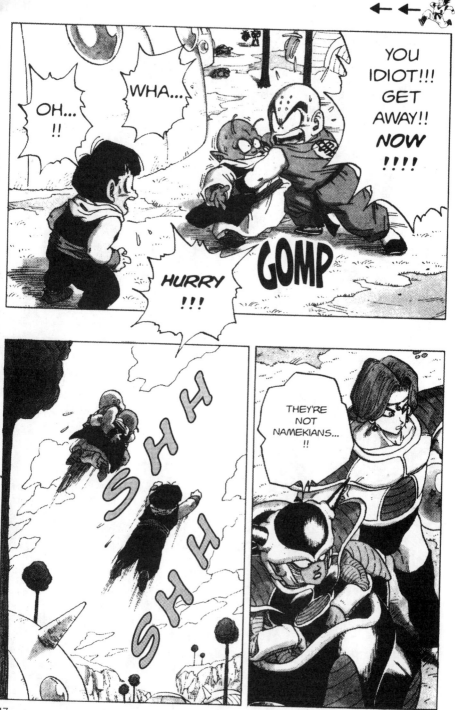

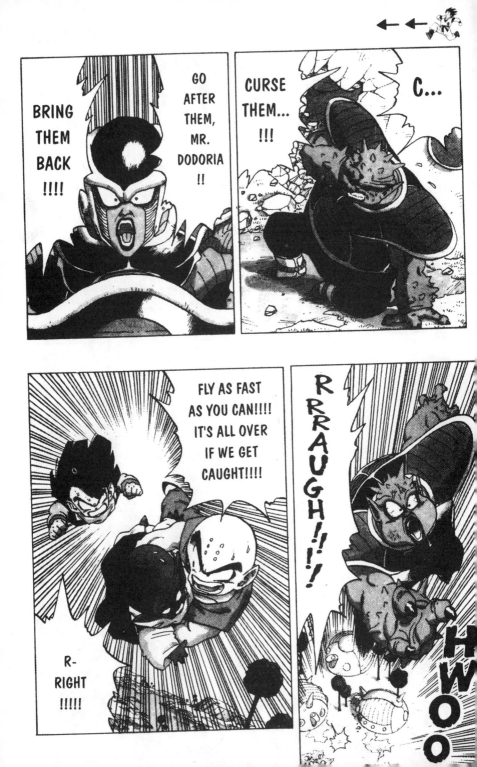

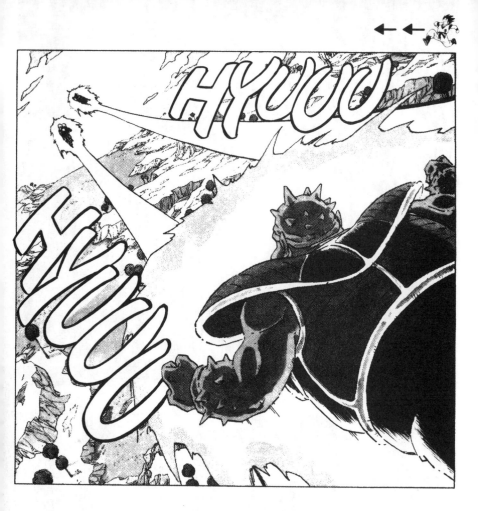

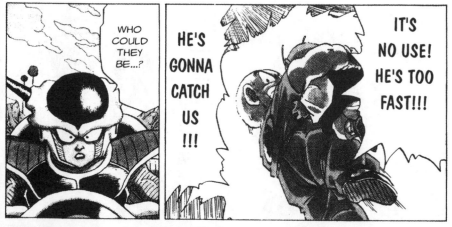

NEXT: *The Hunters and the Hunted*

DBZ:62 • Death in Flight

YOU CAN'T FIGHT SOMEBODY LIKE THIS!!!! JUST *GO*!!!!

LET'S GO DOWN AND FIGHT!!!!

WE CAN'T GET AWAY!!!!

HAAH HA HA !!!

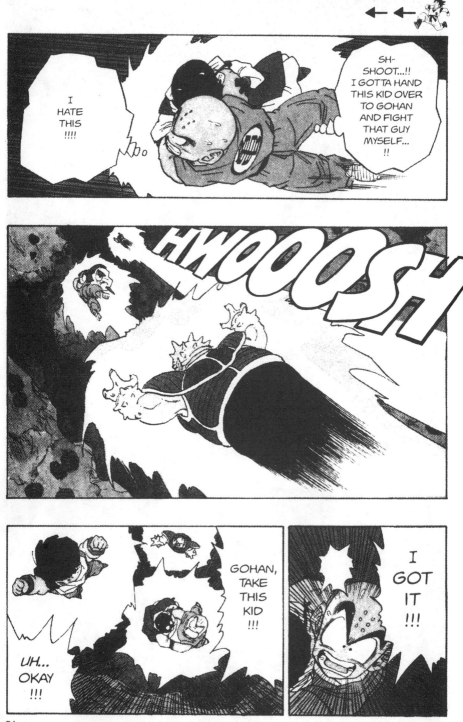

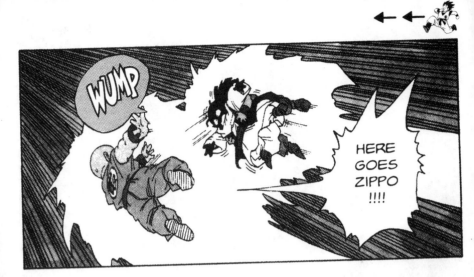

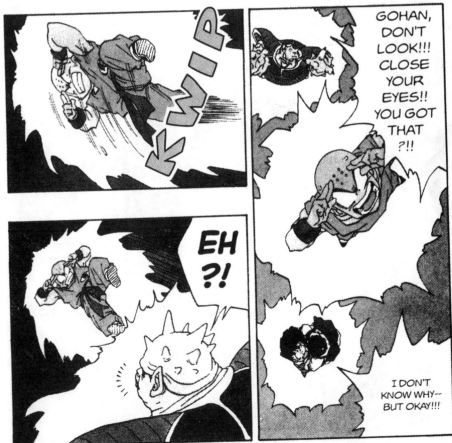

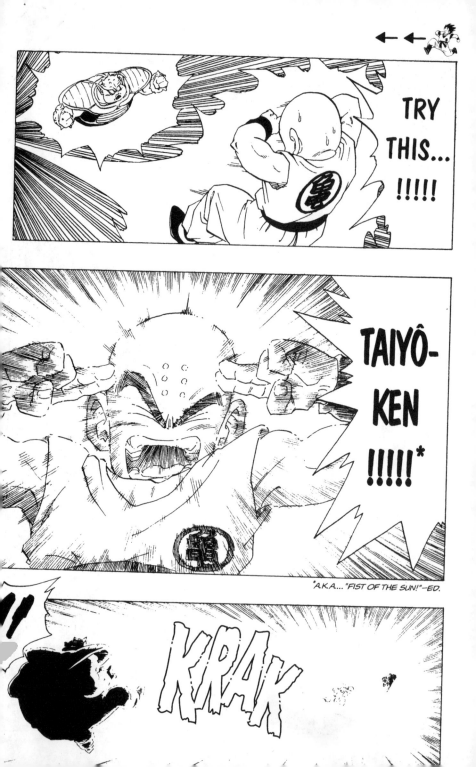

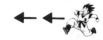

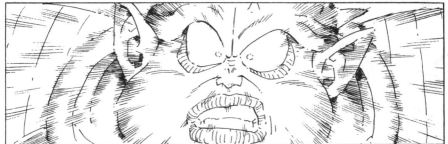

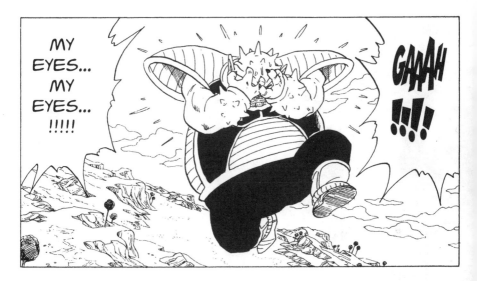

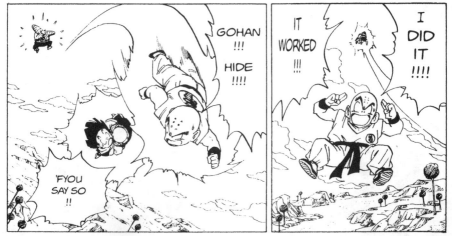

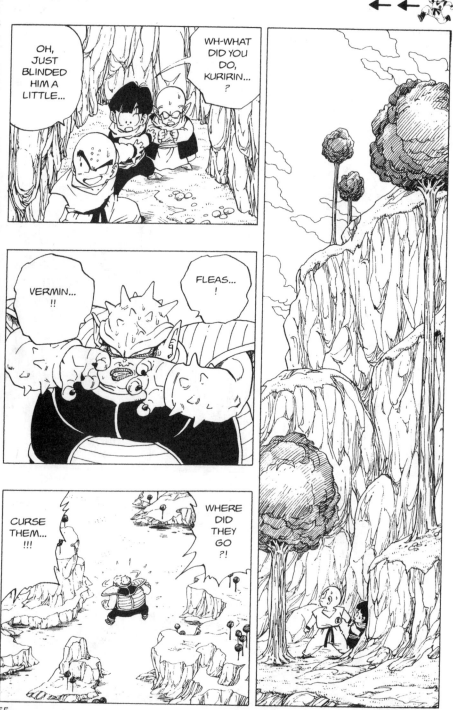

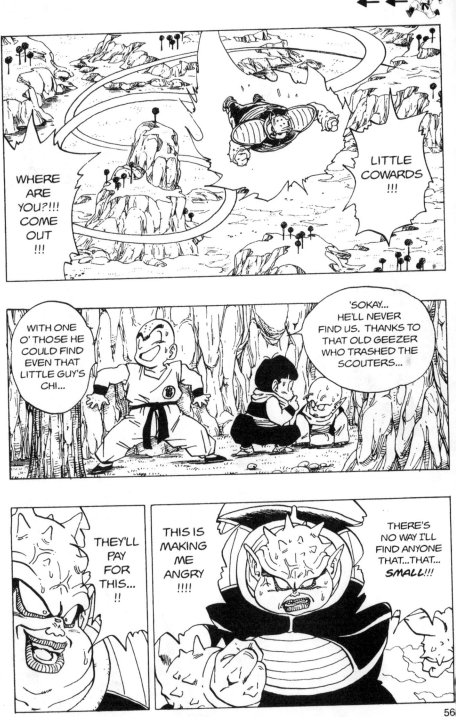

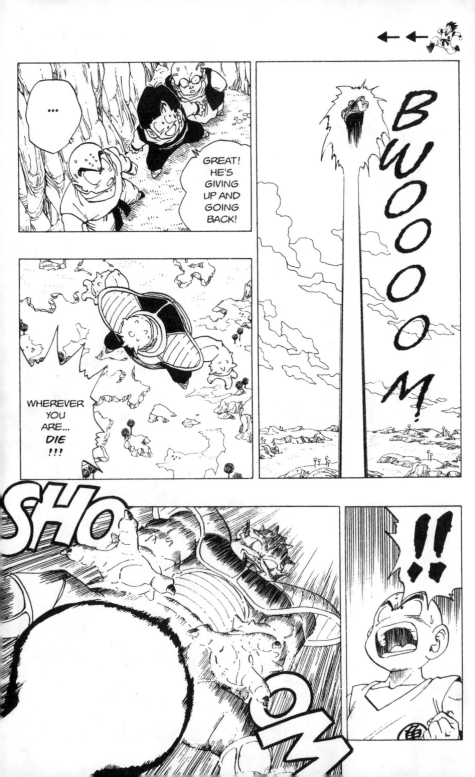

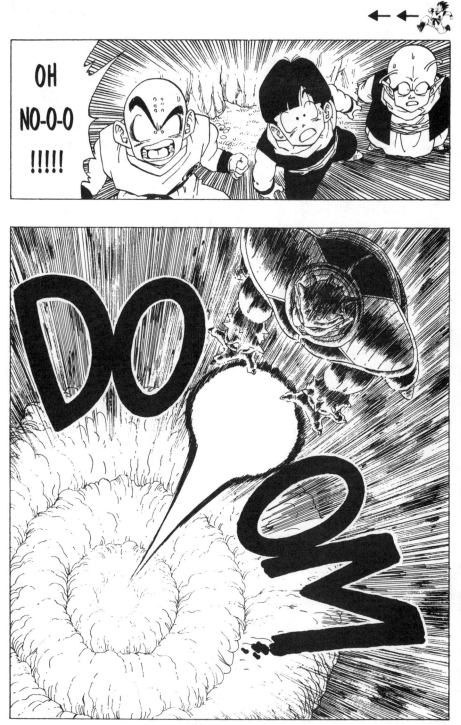

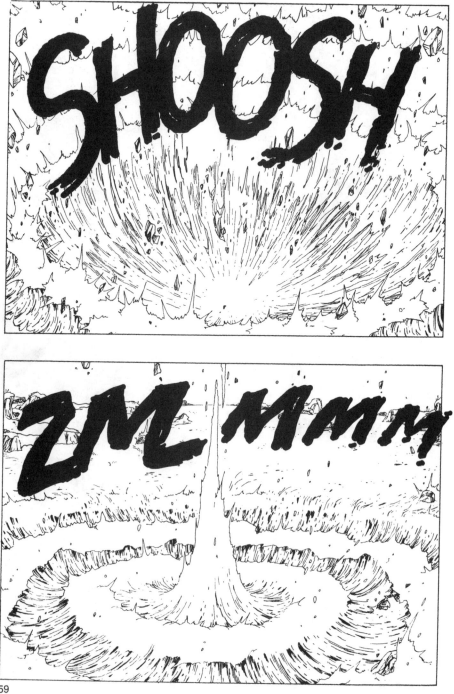

59

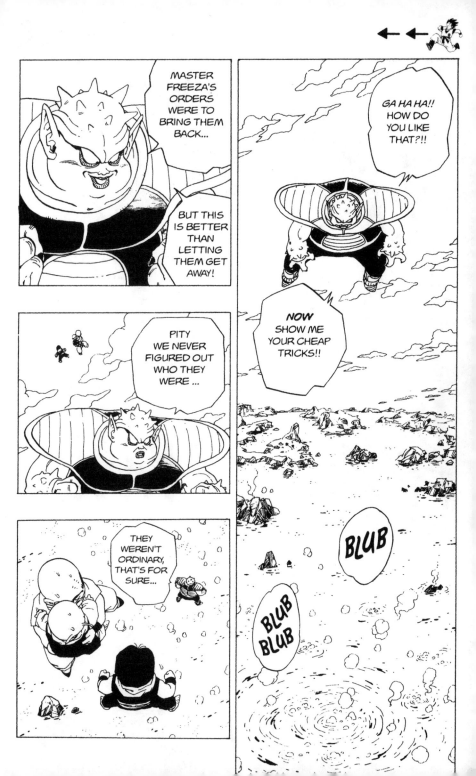

WELL, DOESN'T MAKE ANY DIFFERENCE NOW!

PHEW.

W-WE'RE ALIVE...

THANK YOU FOR SAVING ME...

THANK GOHAN HERE. HE'S THE ONE WHO TOOK THE RISK FOR YOU.

WE GOTTA GET BACK TO WHERE BULMA IS ...

CAN YOU FLY?

Y-YES...

BUT WITHOUT YOU, KURIRIN, WE'D HAVE BOTH DIED.

WHATEVER. LET'S GO!

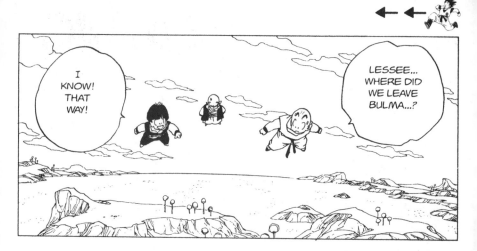

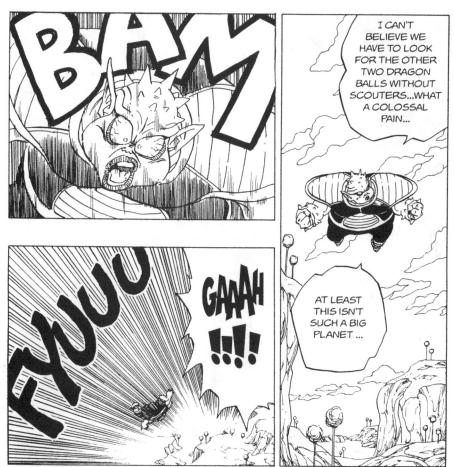

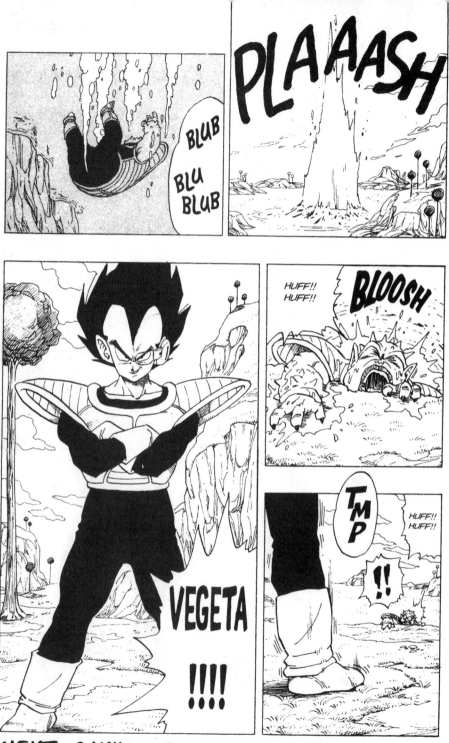

NEXT: A Killer's Fear

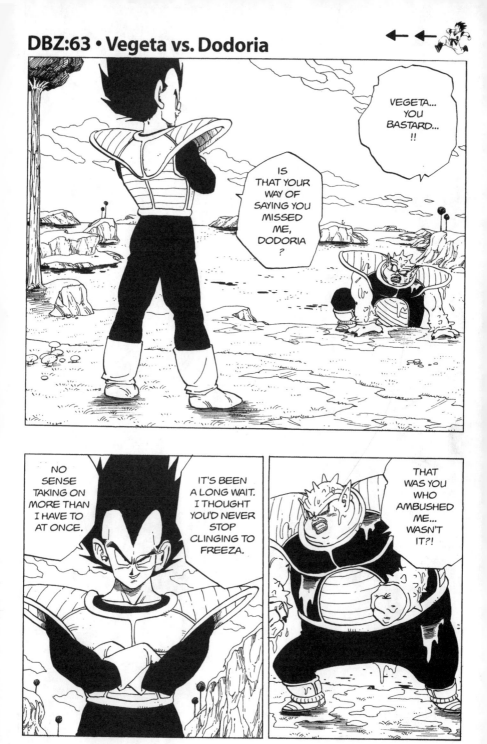

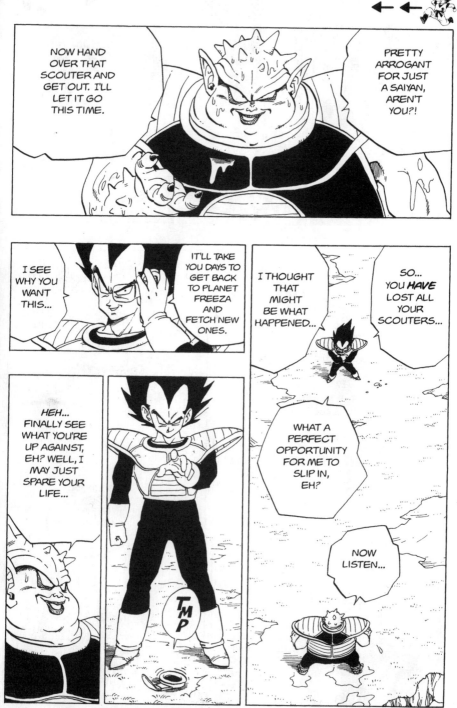

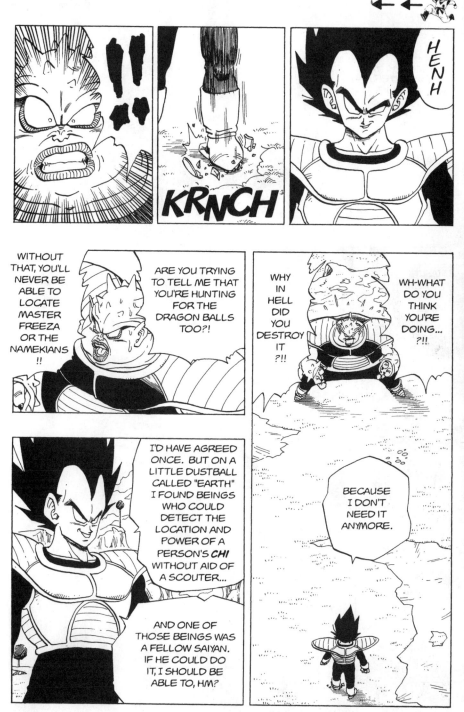

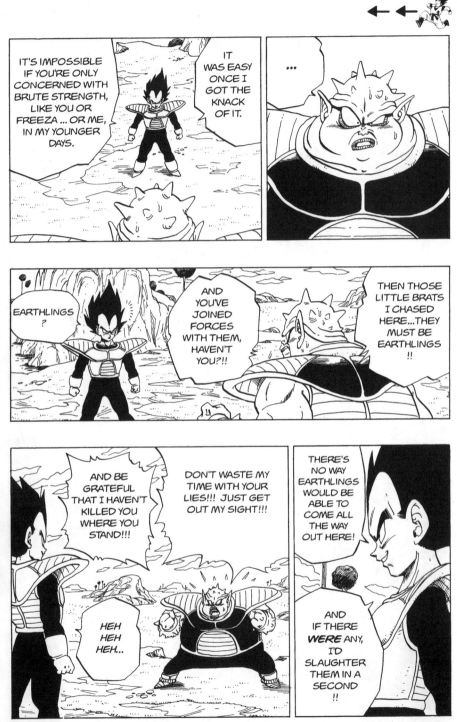

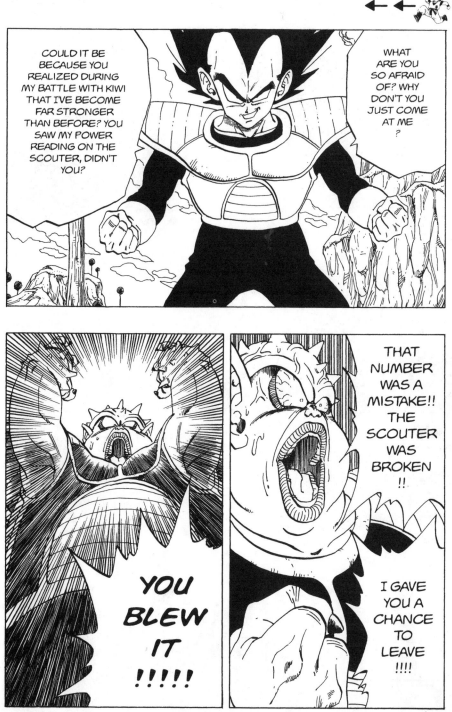

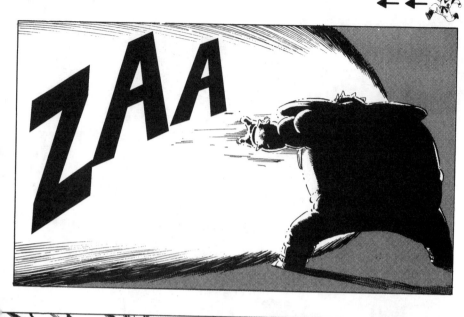

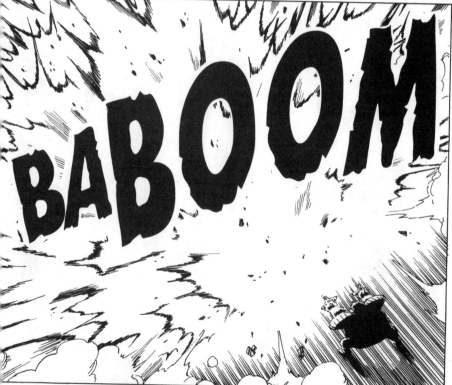

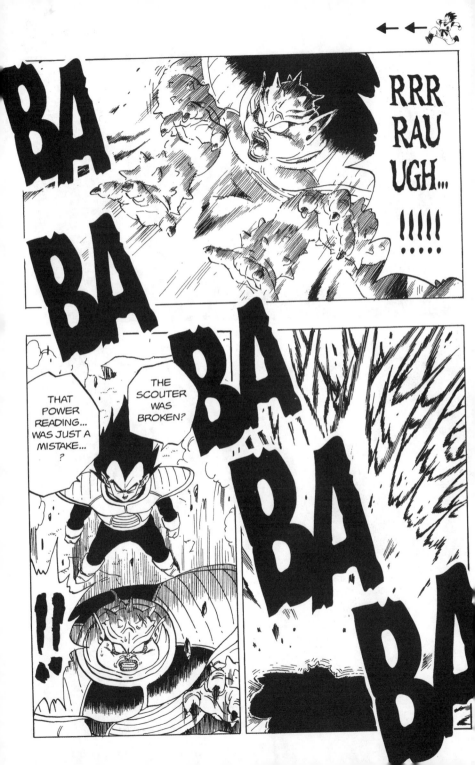

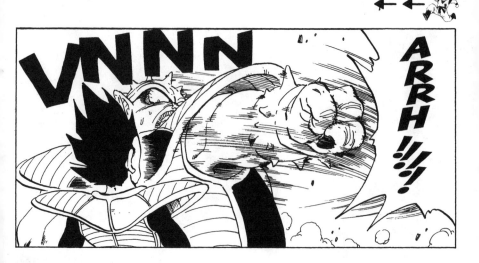

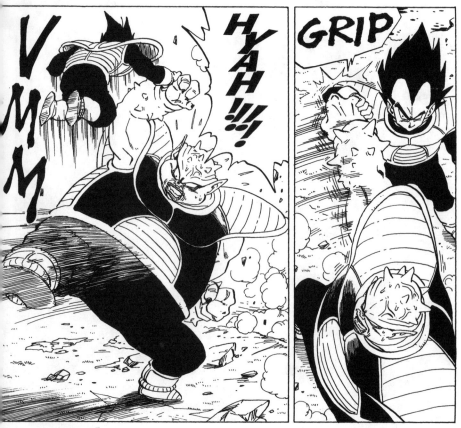

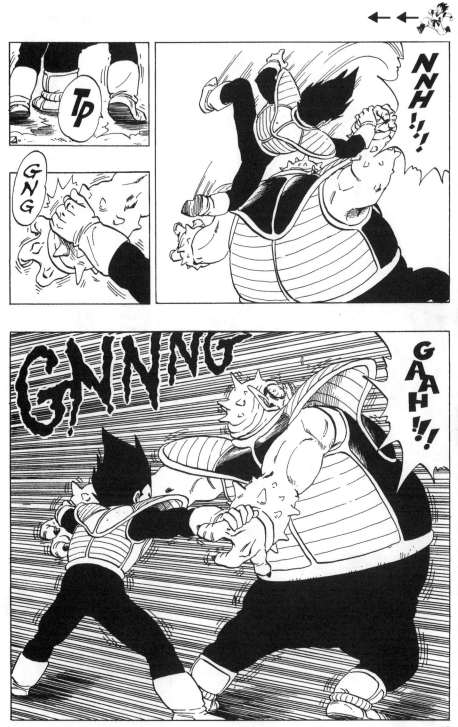

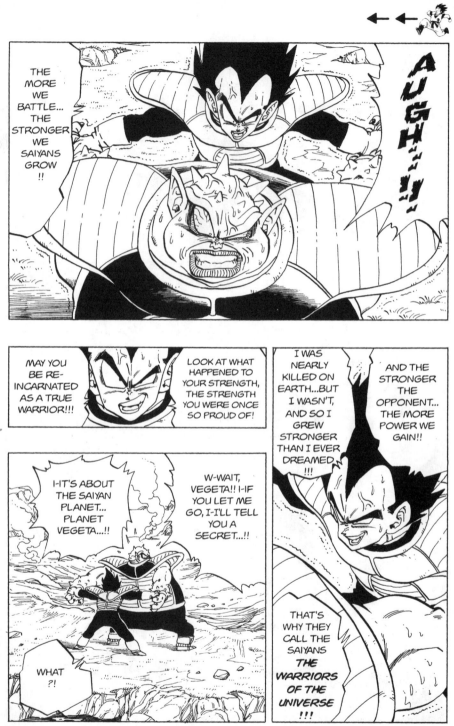

MMF
!!!

PLANET VEGETA?! WHAT IS THERE ABOUT PLANET VEGETA THAT I DON'T KNOW ?!

...BY A METEOR... LIKE MASTER FREEZA... SAID...

Y-YOUR PLANET... IT WASN'T DESTROYED BY A...

TH-THE STRENGTH OF INDIVIDUAL SAIYANS IS NO MATCH FOR M-MASTER FREEZA...

...BUT IF MANY SAIYANS UNITED... IT WOULD BE DIFFICULT EVEN FOR HIM TO DEAL WITH...

WHAT... ?!

YOU...YOU WOULDN'T KILL ME AFTER I TELL YOU... WOULD YOU... ?

IF YOU DON'T TELL ME, I'LL KILL YOU RIGHT NOW !!!

SAY IT !!!!

M-MASTER FREEZA FEARED THAT IF THEY WERE TO BEGIN TAKING POWER... THEY WOULDN'T TAKE ORDERS AS THE SAIYANS ALWAYS HAD. HE DECIDED... IT WAS TIME TO TAKE MEASURES.....

...

AMONG A SMALL PERCENTAGE OF SAIYANS... EXCEPTIONAL WARRIORS SUCH AS YOU BEGAN TO BE BORN...AND WERE INCREASING THEIR NUMBERS...

FF FT

BUT WAIT--DON'T HATE HIM YET!! HE BELIEVED THAT YOU, THE PRINCE OF THE SAIYANS, WOULD PROVE USEFUL!! AND SO HE INTENTIONALLY CHOSE A TIME WHEN YOU WERE NOT ON THE PLANET!!

MASTER FREEZA *HIMSELF* DESTROYED PLANET VEGETA-- AND *YOUR ENTIRE RACE!!*

I COULD CARE LESS ABOUT THE PLANET, MY FELLOW SAIYANS, OR MY PARENTS.

DON'T GET ME WRONG, DODORIA.

SNORT

HMPH. SORRY IF THE SHOCK WAS TOO GREAT.

I THINK I'LL TAKE THIS CHANCE TO RETURN TO THE MASTER.

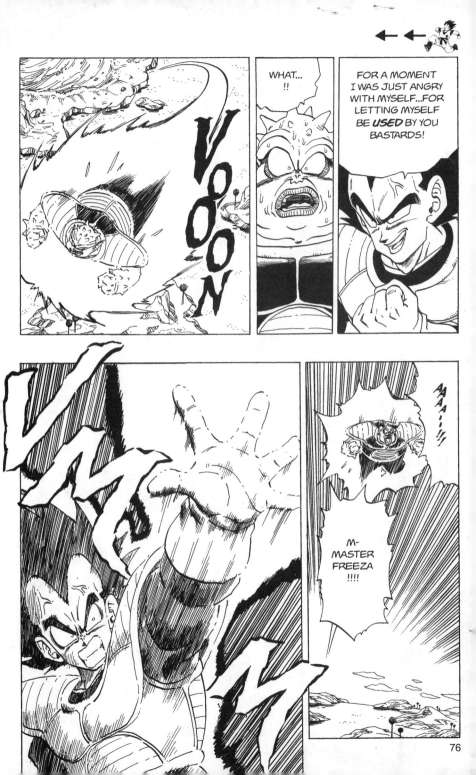

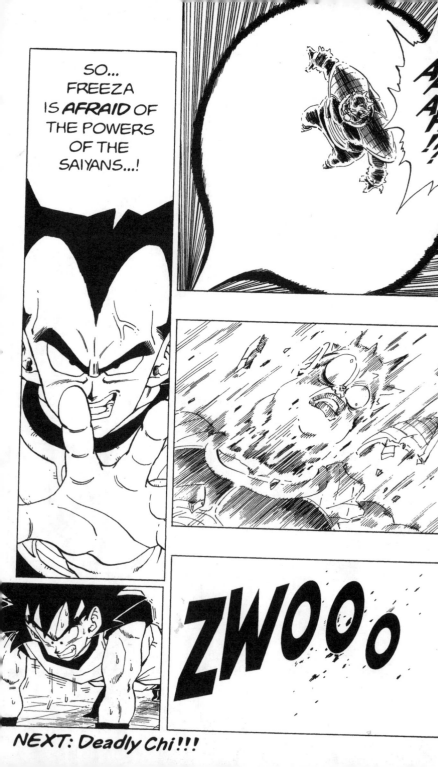

NEXT: *Deadly Chi!!!*

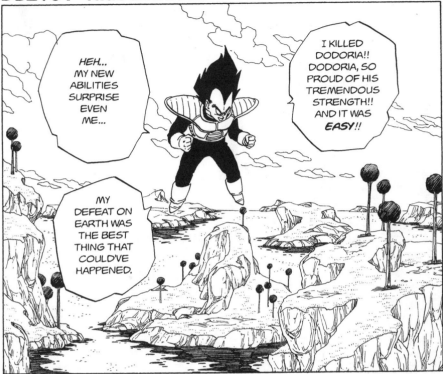

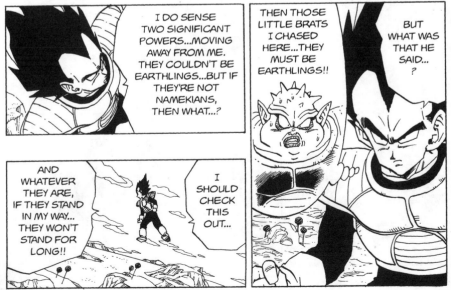

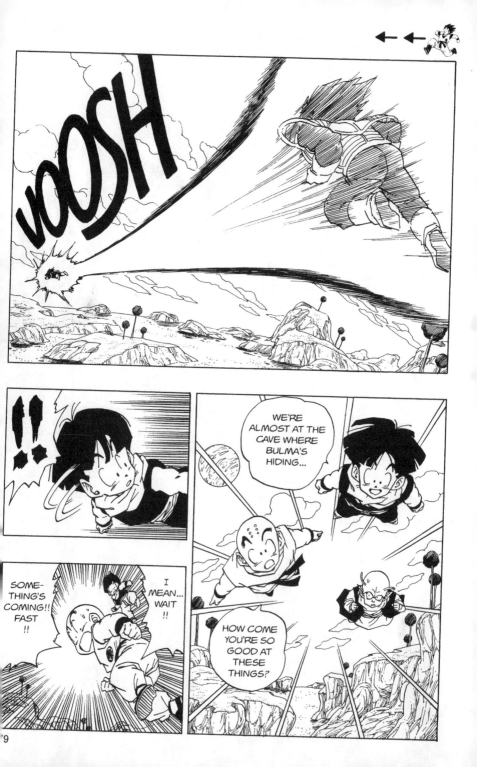

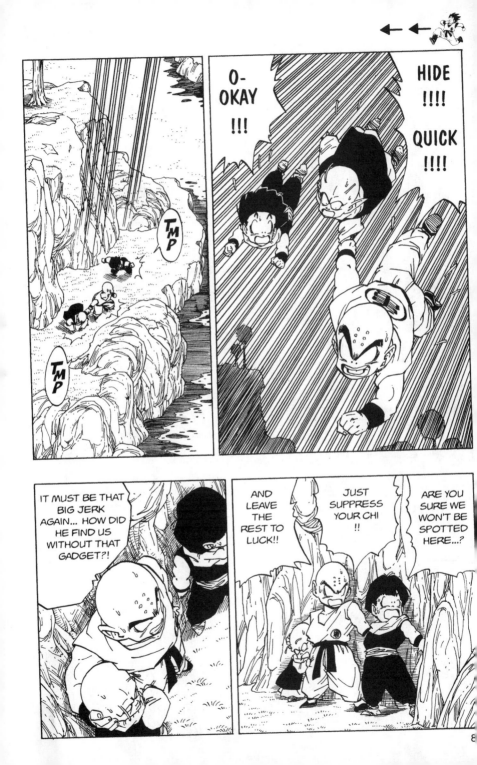

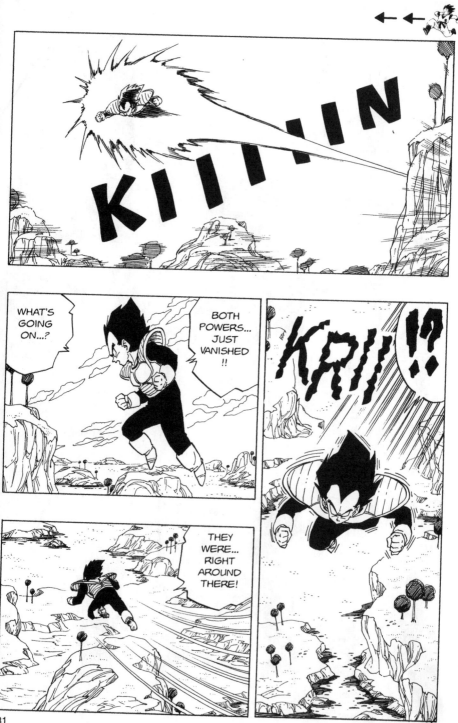

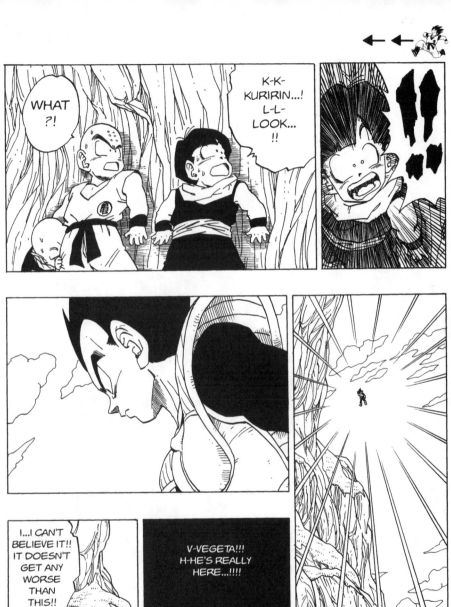

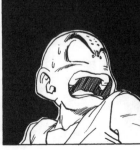

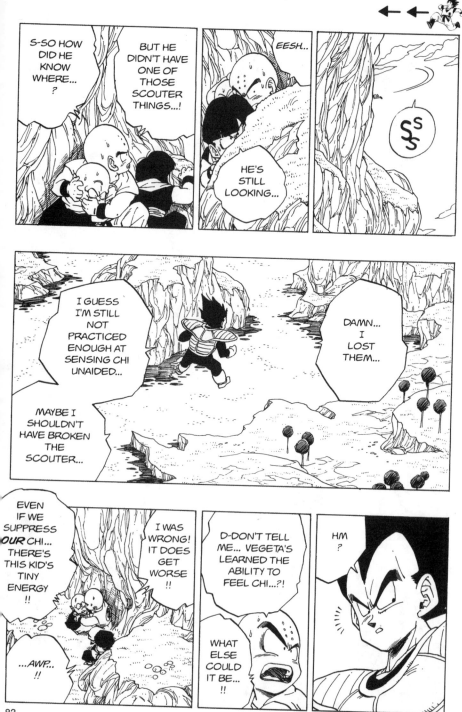

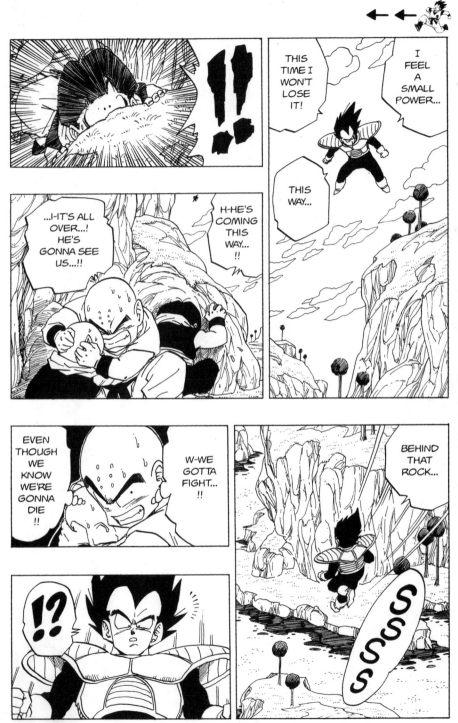

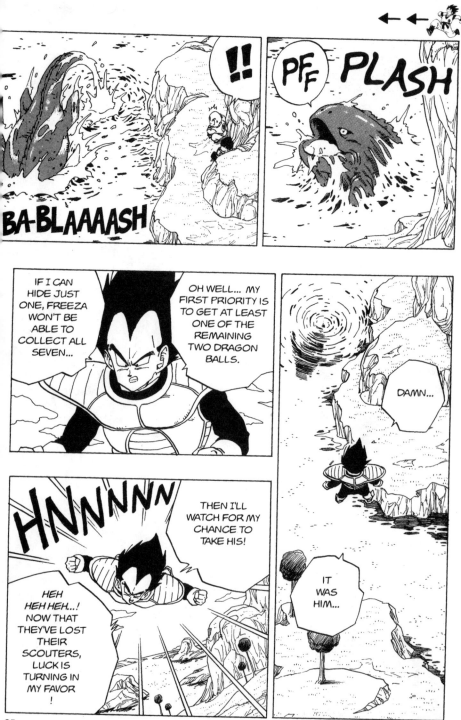

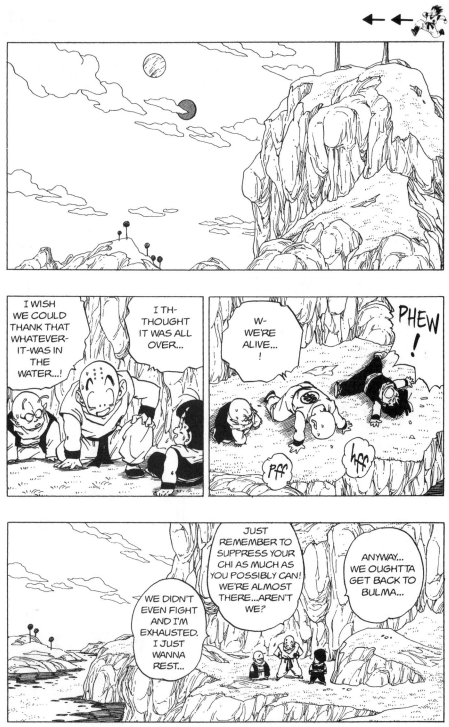

POING!

TP

OH... YEAH.

LOOK KURIRIN! THERE IT IS.

I MEAN, I FEEL BAD FOR YAMCHA AND EVERYBODY WHO DIED...

BUT INSTEAD OF US BRINGIN' THEM BACK TO LIFE, WE'RE MORE LIKELY JUST TO MAKE SOME NEW CORPSES... *OURS!*

MAN... I'M STARTING TO THINK THAT WE NEVER SHOULD'VE COME TO THIS PLANET...

SHE MUST BE HIDING DEEP IN THE CAVE...

BULMA!

HUH? SHE'S NOT HERE...

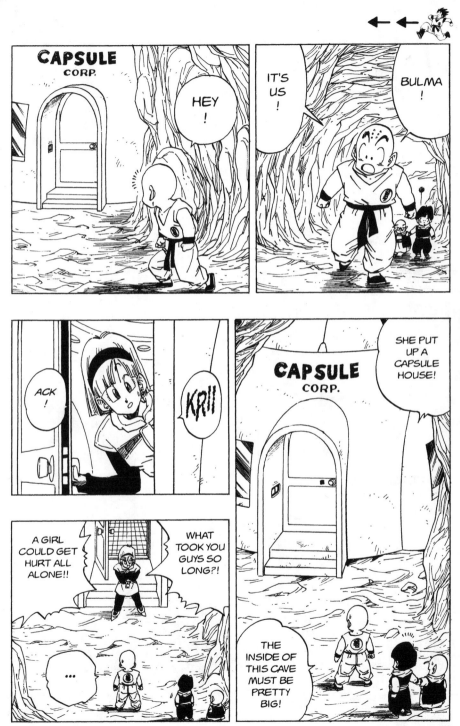

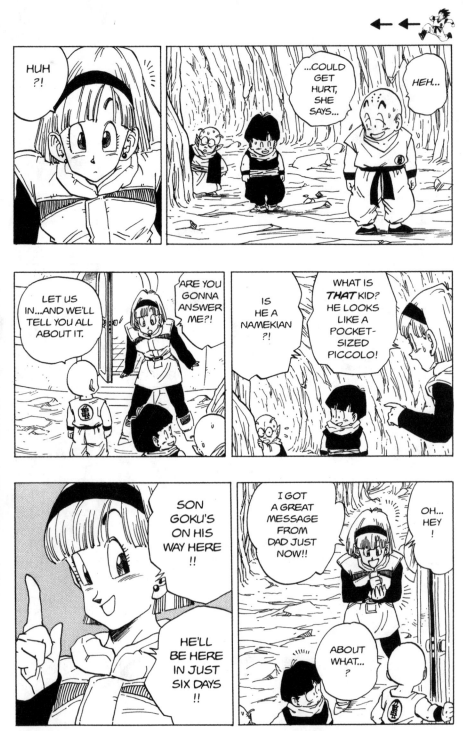

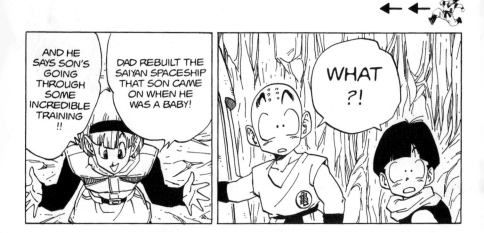

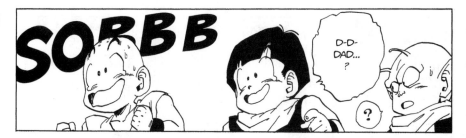

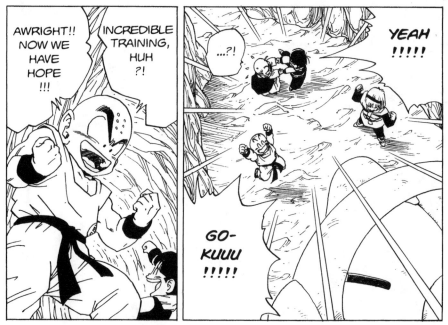

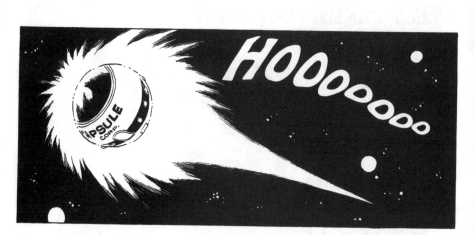

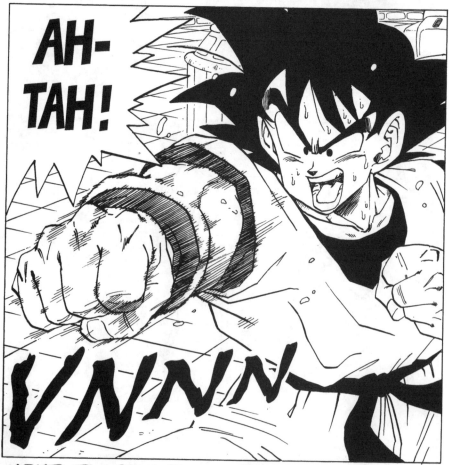

NEXT: The Sixth Dragon Ball

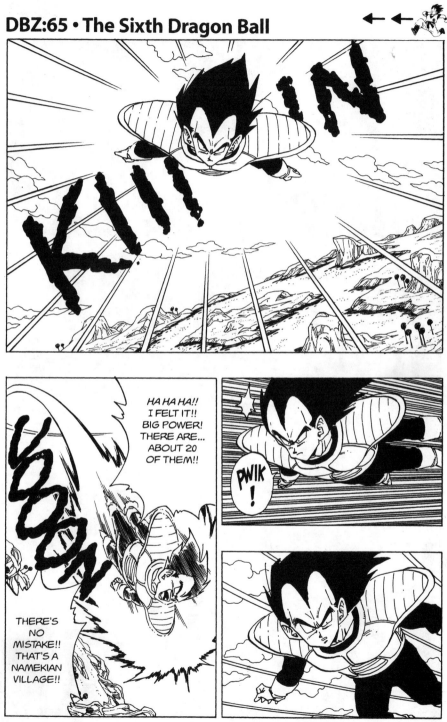

AND THEY MUST HAVE A DRAGON BALL!

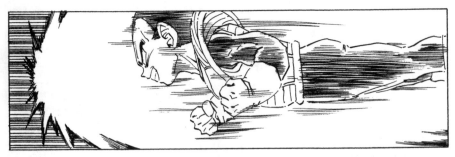

NO MATTER WHAT I DO-- THEY CAN'T TRACK ME!!!

HAHAHAAA!! AND FREEZA AND HIS MEN HAVE LOST THEIR SCOUTERS !!!

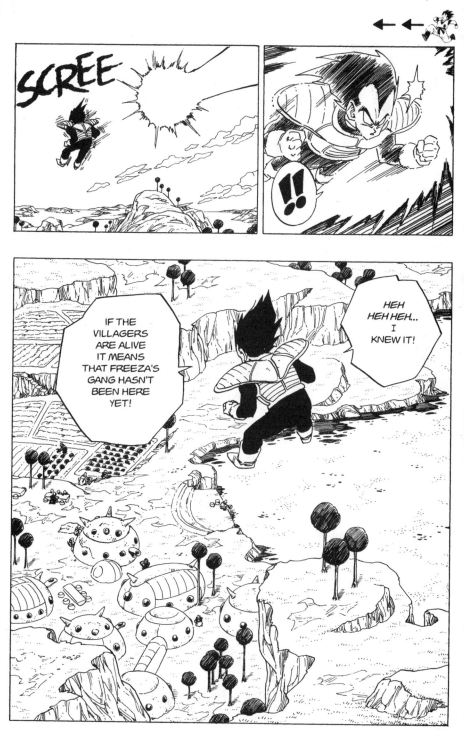

TUMP

!!

!!

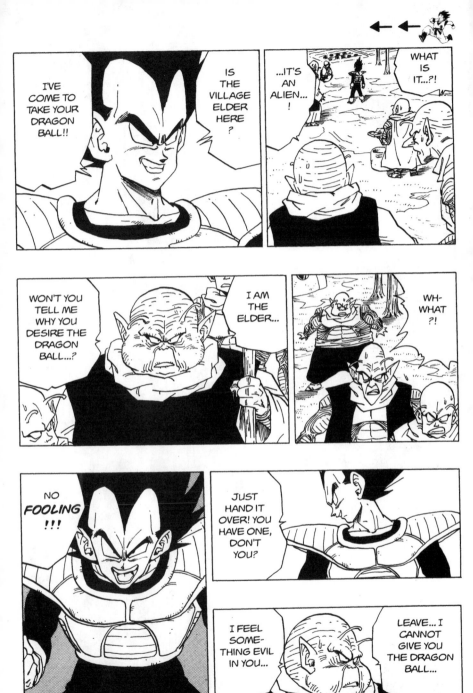

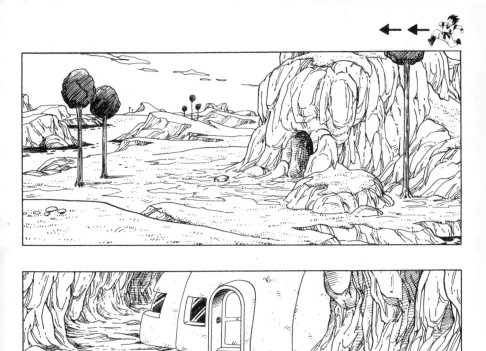

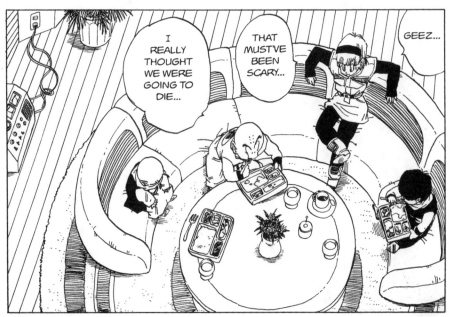

OH YEAH...

I DON'T BLAME HIM... MOST OF THE PEOPLE IN HIS VILLAGE WERE KILLED, WEREN'T THEY...?

...

NOT LIKE IT'S GOOD OR ANYTHING, BUT...

YOU SHOULD EAT, DON'T BE SHY.

THOSE WERE YOUNG HYDRANGEA PLANTS...

BUT YOUR VILLAGE HAD A FIELD AND WAS GROWING SOME KIND OF VEGETABLE.

HUH ?

WE JUST NEED WATER...

WE DON'T EAT FOOD LIKE THIS...

SAY, WHAT'S YOUR NAME?

...

BUT THE HYDRANGEA FORESTS... AND MOST OF THE NAMEKIANS DIED OFF...

THEY SAY THAT A LONG TIME AGO, BEFORE THE TERRIBLE DROUGHT CAME, NAMEK WAS A BEAUTIFUL WORLD WITH LOTS OF HYDRANGEAS...

UMM... WHO ARE YOU PEOPLE?

DENDE...

SO WE'RE GROWING HYDRANGEA TREES TO MAKE OUR PLANET BEAUTIFUL AGAIN.

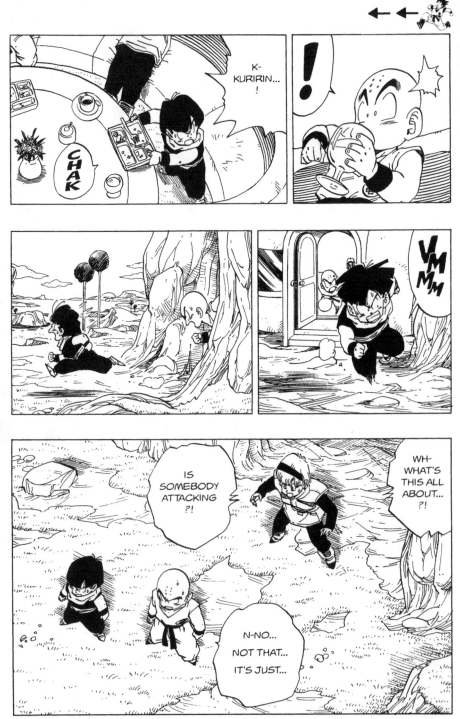

N-NAMEKIANS ARE BEING KILLED AGAIN...!

WHAT ?!

THE *CHI* ARE GETTING WEAKER... ONE BY ONE...

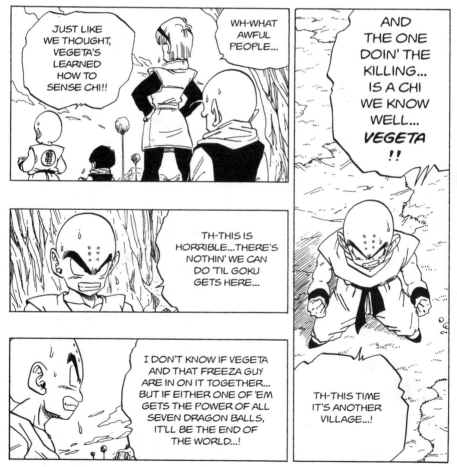

JUST LIKE WE THOUGHT, VEGETA'S LEARNED HOW TO SENSE CHI!!

WH-WHAT AWFUL PEOPLE...

AND THE ONE DOIN' THE KILLING... IS A CHI WE KNOW WELL... *VEGETA* !!

TH-THIS IS HORRIBLE...THERE'S NOTHIN' WE CAN DO 'TIL GOKU GETS HERE...

I DON'T KNOW IF VEGETA AND THAT FREEZA GUY ARE IN ON IT TOGETHER... BUT IF EITHER ONE OF 'EM GETS THE POWER OF ALL SEVEN DRAGON BALLS, IT'LL BE THE END OF THE WORLD...!

TH-THIS TIME IT'S ANOTHER VILLAGE...!

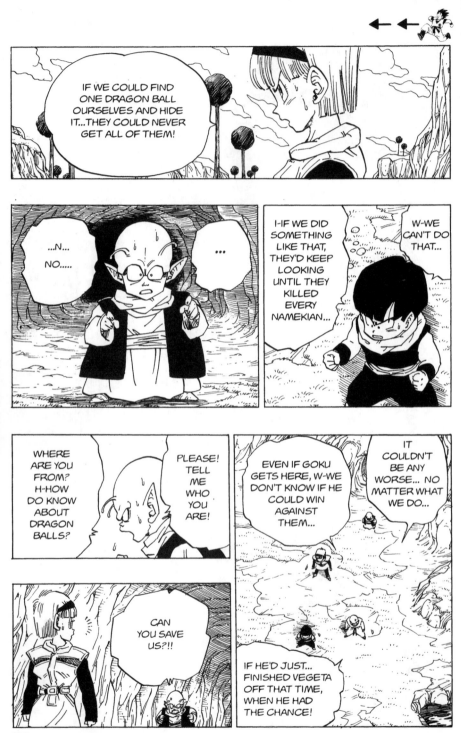

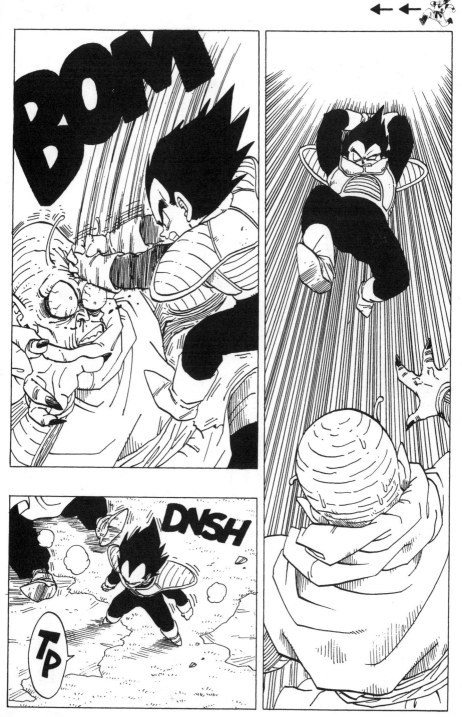

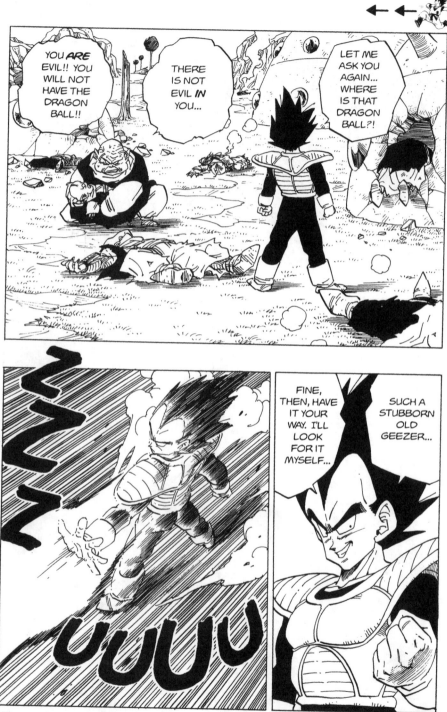

NOW WE WANT TO BRING OUR FRIENDS BACK TO LIFE BY USING YOUR PLANET'S DRAGON BALLS...

...AND *HE* WAS THE NAMEKIAN WHO ESCAPED TO EARTH.

ALL RIGHT...

...I'LL START HERE...

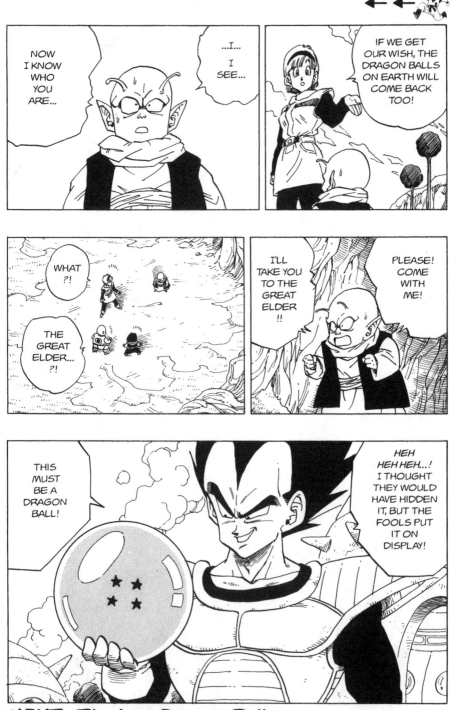

NEXT: *The Last Dragon Ball*

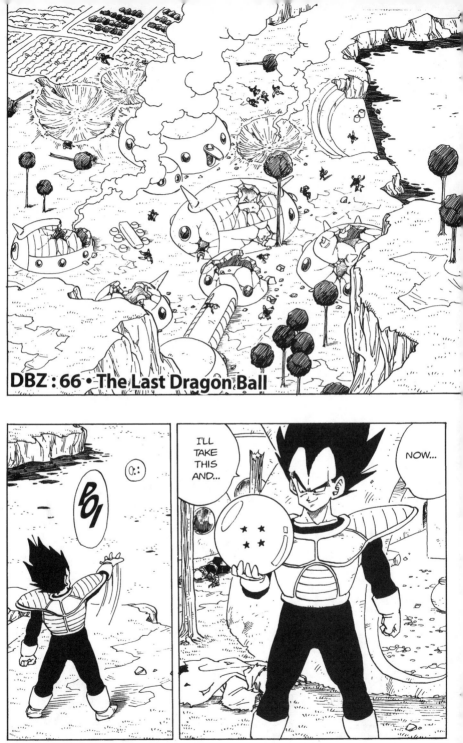

DBZ : 66 • The Last Dragon Ball

...I'M
THE ONLY
ONE WHO
KNOWS...

HEH HEH HEH...
NO ONE WILL
FIND THIS DRAGON
BALL IF I SINK
IT HERE...

WHAT
SHOULD
I DO
NOW...?

I MAY
AS WELL
LOOK FOR
THE LAST
ONE...

FREEZA
HAS
FIVE
DRAGON
BALLS...

HYUUU

DODORIA IS TAKING TOO LONG... DO YOU THINK HE'S STILL CHASING AFTER THOSE LITTLE WEIRDLINGS...?

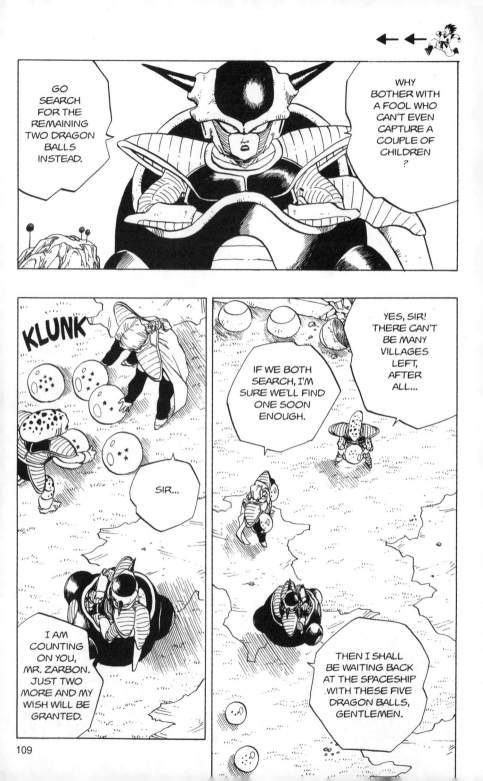

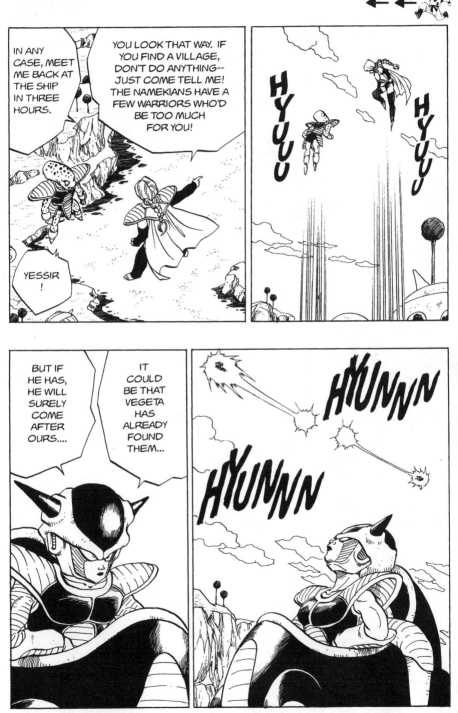

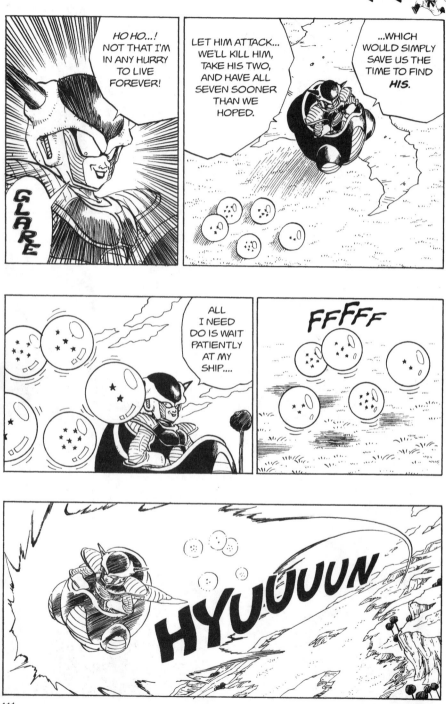

WHO'S THE GREAT ELDER...?

WHAT?!

THE GR... GR...?!

HOW...? WE LAY EGGS THROUGH OUR MOUTHS... HOW ELSE?

...THE LONE... W-WAIT...HOW DO YOU PEOPLE HAVE CHILDREN?!

THE LONE SURVIVOR OF THE TERRIBLE DROUGHT AND GIVER OF LIFE TO US ALL.

THE PARENT OF ALL PEOPLE ON PLANET NAMEK.

TH-THEN THE GREAT ELDER MUST BE A WOMAN...

Y-YEAH..... HOW ELSE...?

I'M THE 108TH CHILD OF THE GREAT ELDER.

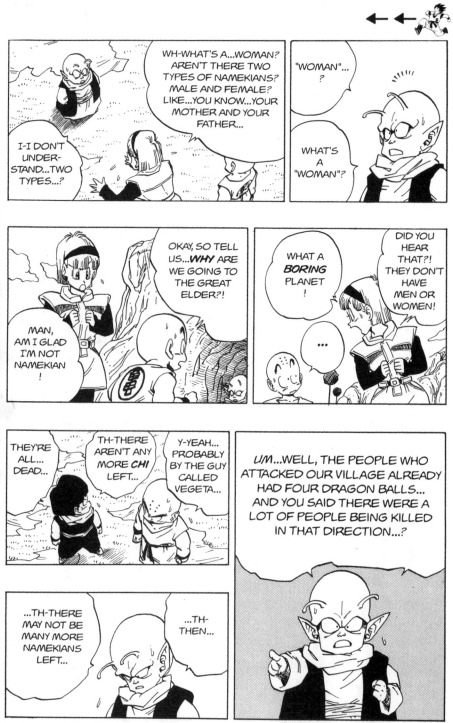

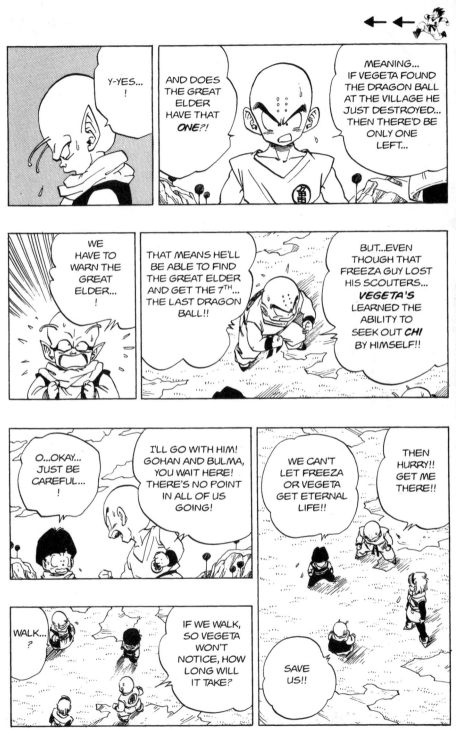

114

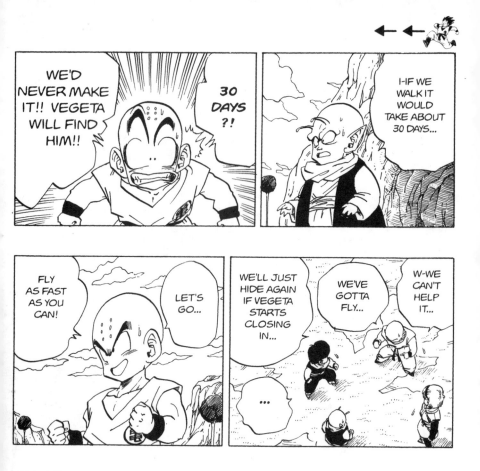

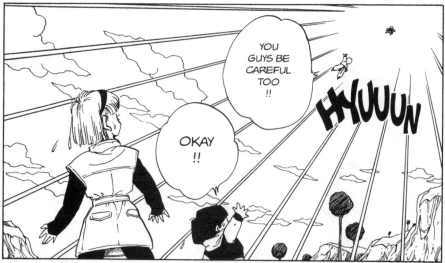

ANYWAY, WE'VE GOTTA GET THE GREAT ELDER'S DRAGON BALL...AND HIDE IT FOR THE FIVE OR SIX DAYS 'TIL GOKU GETS HERE! AFTER THAT, ALL WE CAN HOPE FOR IS ONE OF GOKU'S MIRACLES...

IT SEEMS LIKE VEGETA'S GOTTEN EVEN STRONGER... AND I FELT AN EVEN *MORE* POWERFUL CHI FROM THAT FREEZA WHOEVER-HE-IS...

DANG IT... MY LIFE'S ENDING AND I DON'T HAVE A SINGLE GIRLFRIEND TO SHOW FOR IT....

HEH... THEY SAY ONCE YOU START HOPING FOR MIRACLES IT'S ALL OVER...

I DON'T KNOW WHAT KIND OF TRAINING GOKU'S DOING... BUT I'VE GOT A FEELING IT WON'T BE ENOUGH...

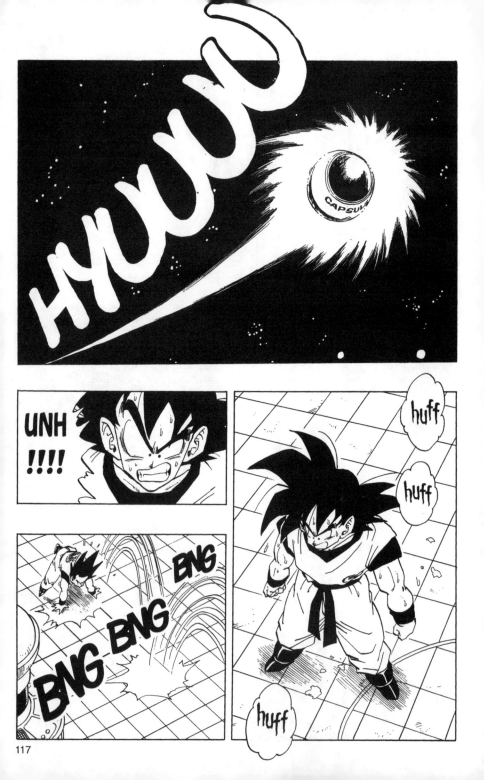

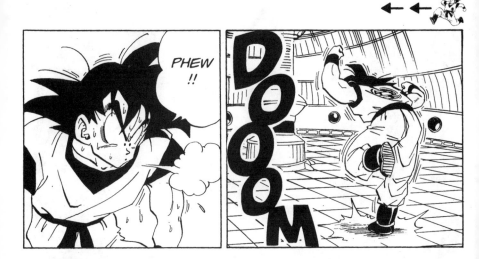

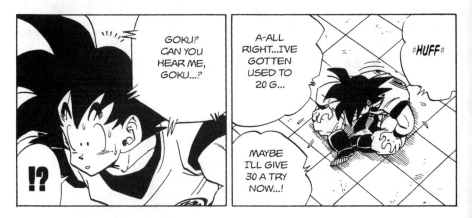

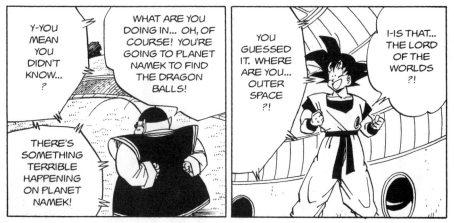

118

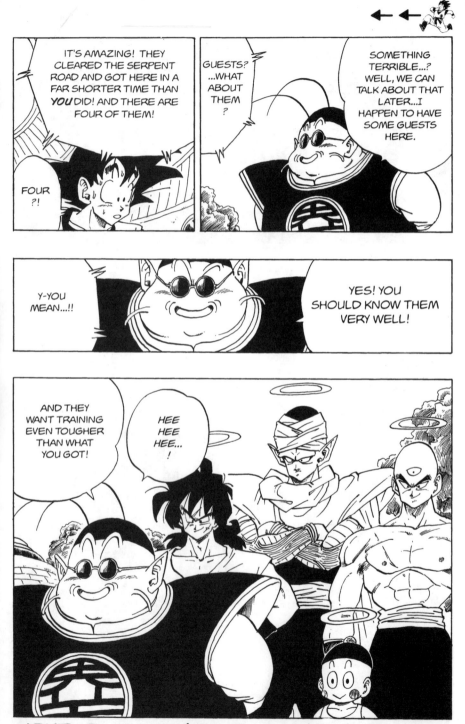

NEXT: *Even a Lord Can Be Surprised...!*

DBZ:67 • The Four Dead Heroes

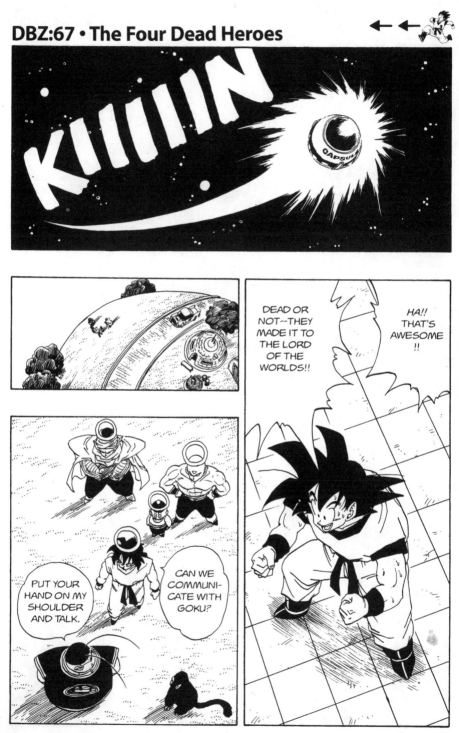

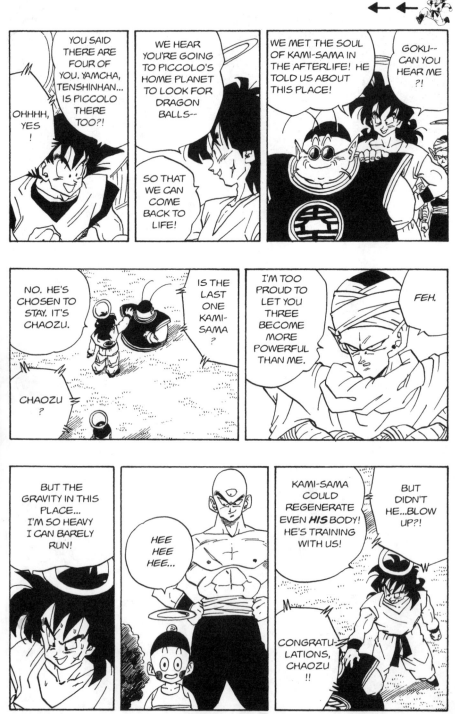

121

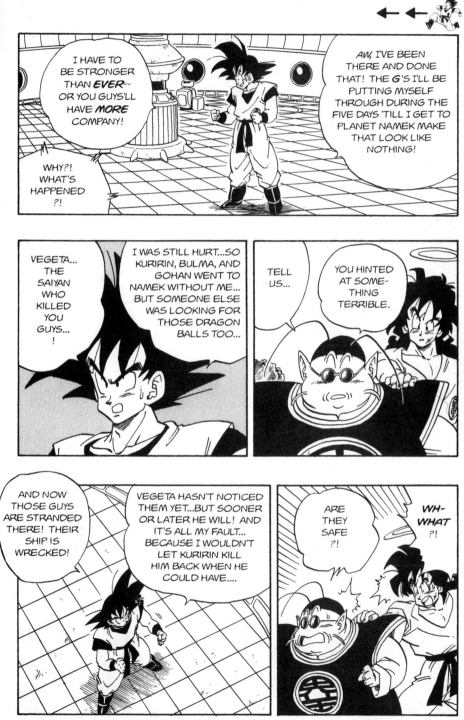

THERE ARE **OTHER** CREATURES AFTER THE DRAGON BALLS, TOO... ALL WEARING THE SAME UNIFORM AS VEGETA... AND ONE OF THEM HAS A **CHI** POWER THAT EXCEEDS VEGETA'S... BY A LONG SHOT!

BUT EVEN THAT...MAY NOT BE THE WORST THING...

WAY!!

NO

I'LL LET YOU KNOW AS SOON AS I FIND OUT...

IS HIS NAME... B-BY ANY CHANCE... FREEZA?

WHAT DID HE SAY?!

A-AND VEGETA... WAS TOO MUCH... EVEN FOR GOKU...

......
......

IF IT IS.......

123

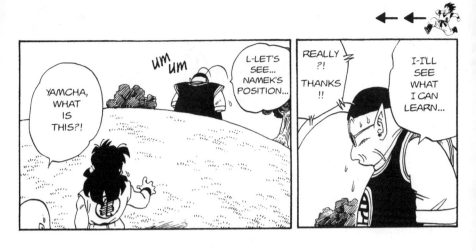

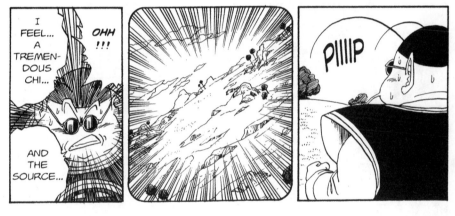

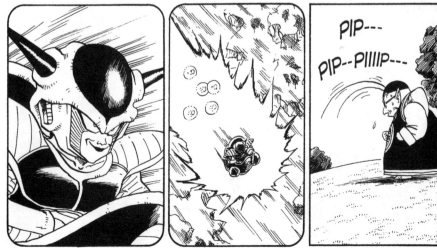

BUT NOT THIS TIME, SON! *NO ONE* CAN HANDLE THIS ONE! JUST STAY *AWAY*!

GOKU... YOUR GREATEST STRENGTH HAS ALWAYS BEEN YOUR BELIEF THAT YOU CAN HANDLE ANYTHING....

FREEZA!!!

WHEN YOU REACH NAMEK, JUST GRAB THE THREE OF THEM AND *RUN AWAY*!!

GOKU, I COMMAND YOU!!

B-BUT WHAT...?

...HUH...?

MY LORD-- DO YOU KNOW HIM?!

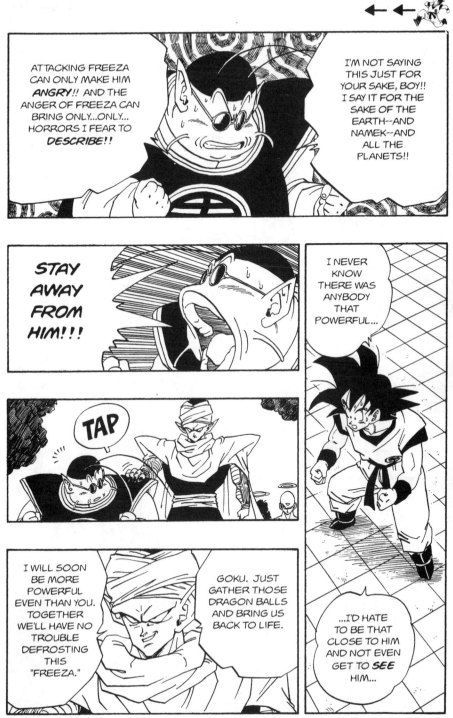

126

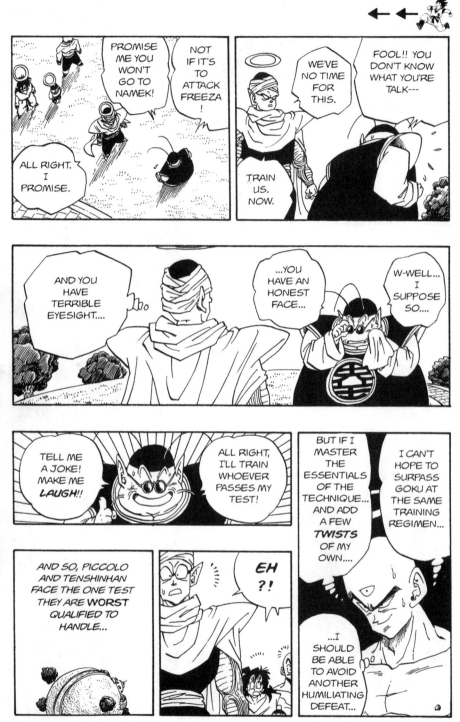

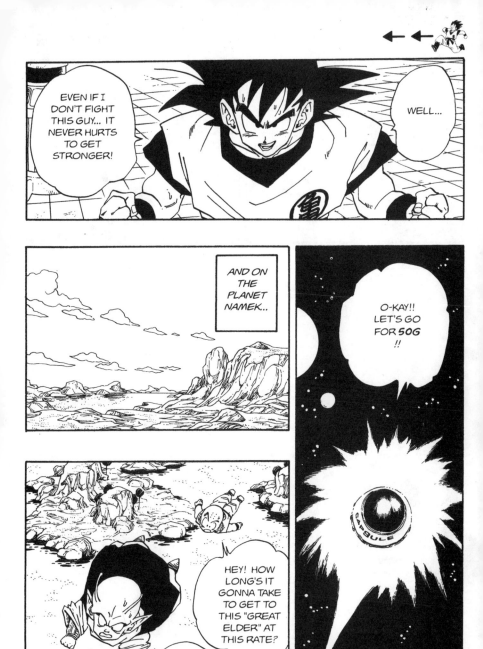

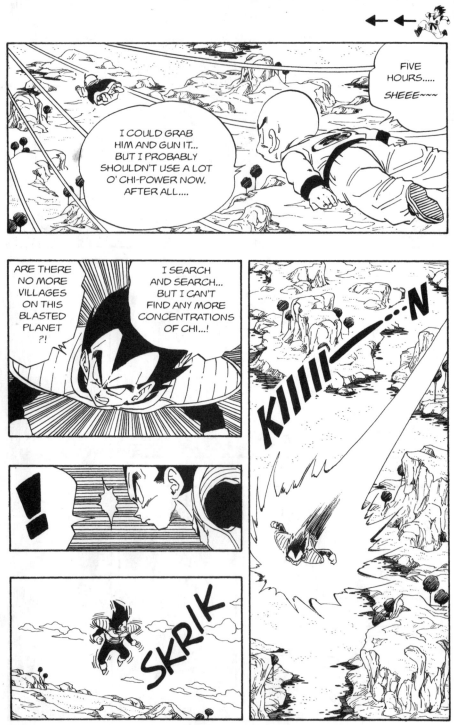

129

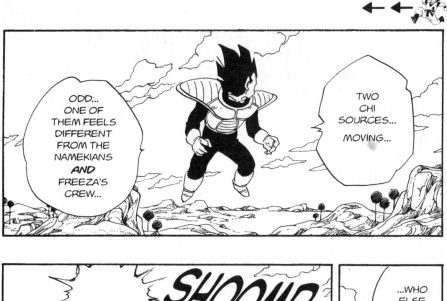

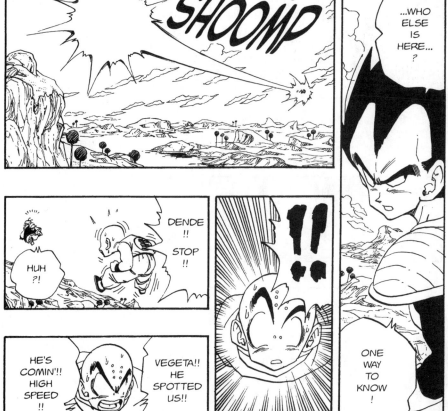

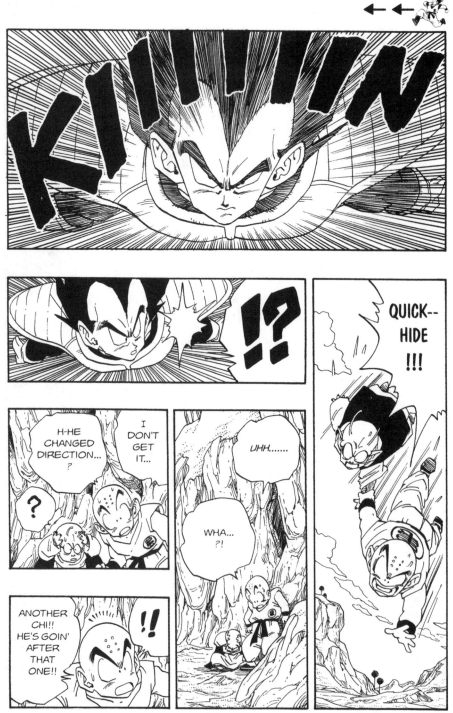

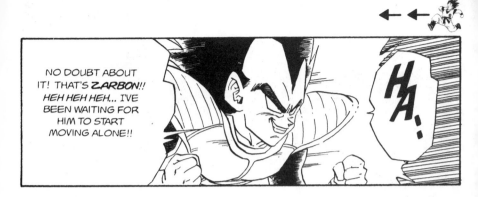

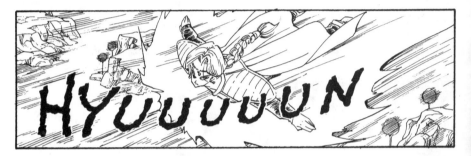

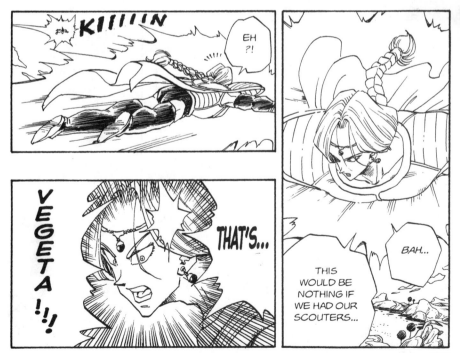

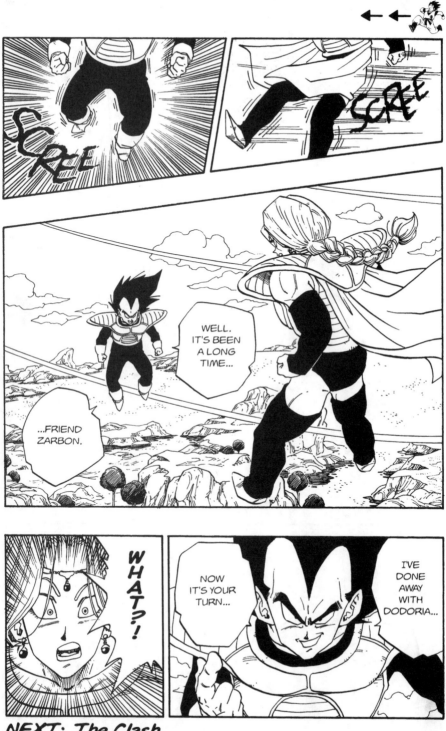

NEXT: *The Clash*

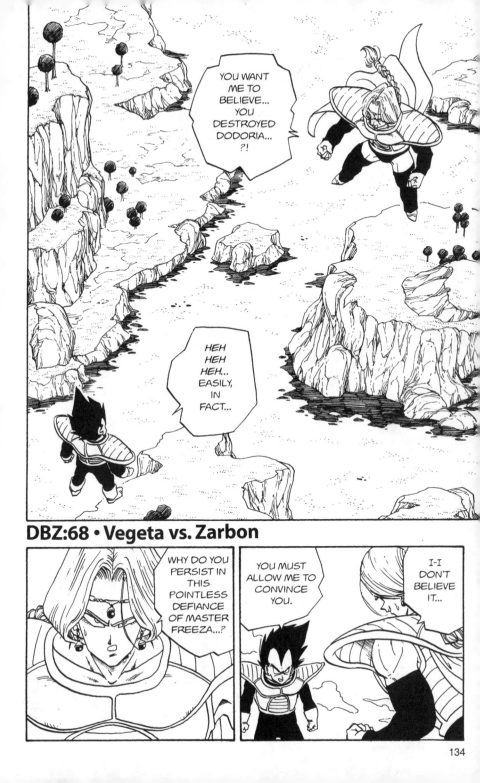

DBZ:68 • Vegeta vs. Zarbon

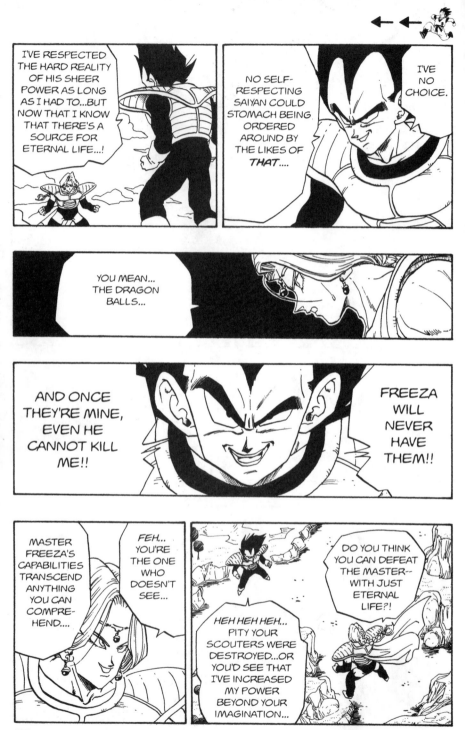

135

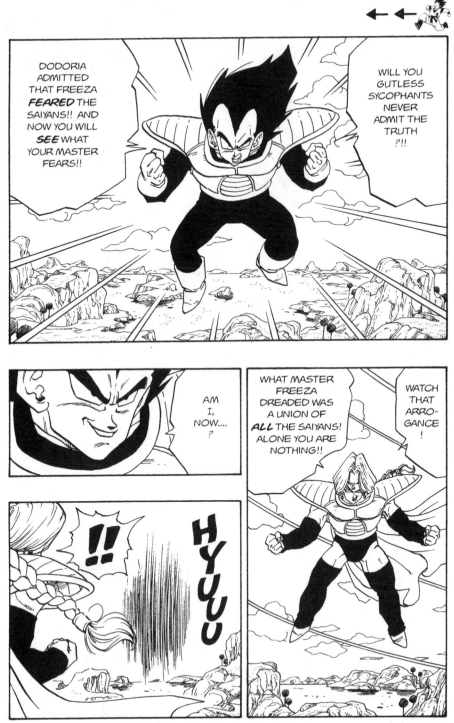

EH
?!

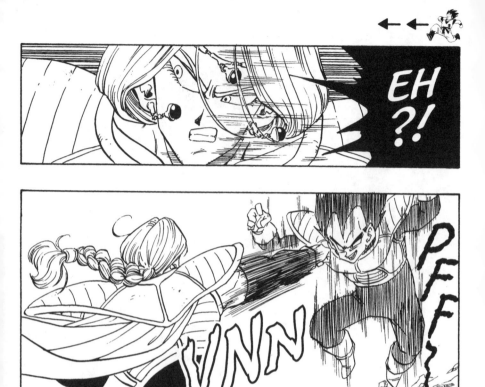

PFF...

VNN

HYOH!!!

BASH

NH...

NNH......

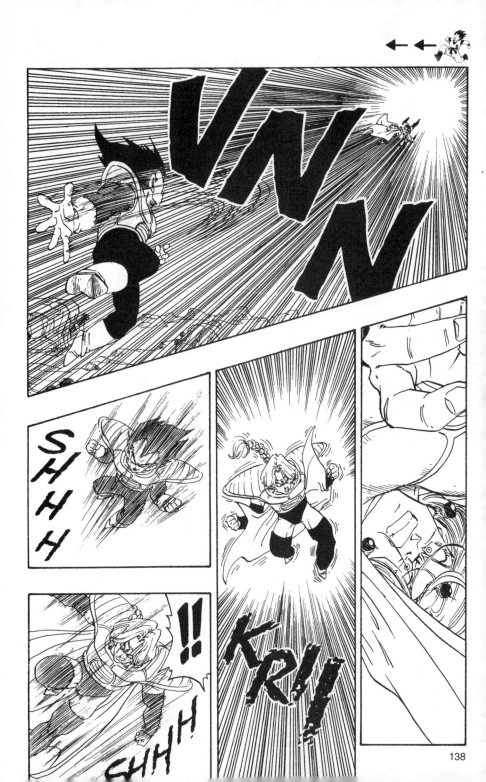

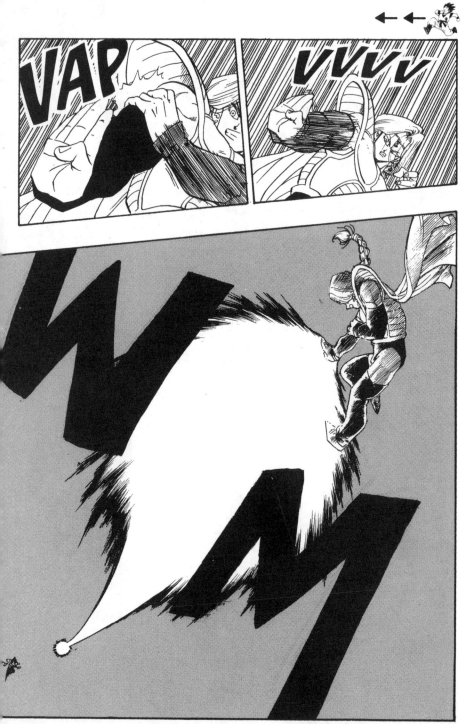

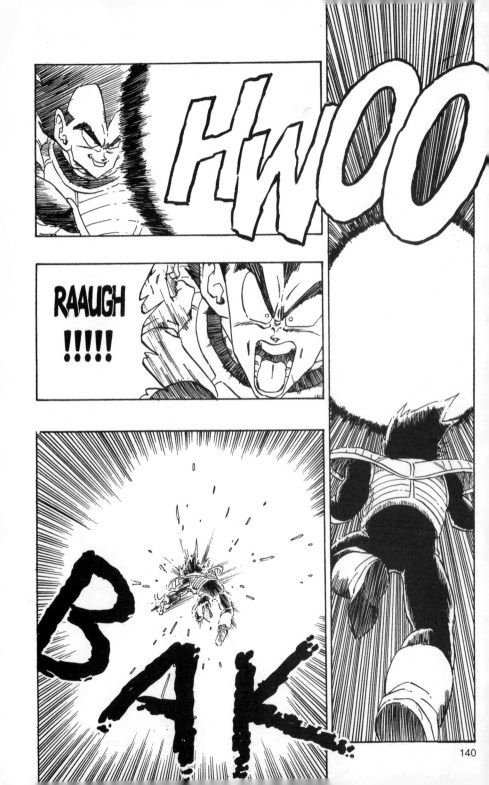

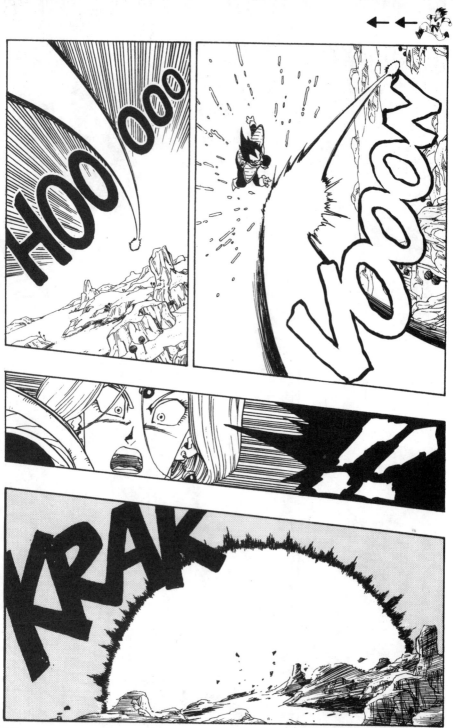

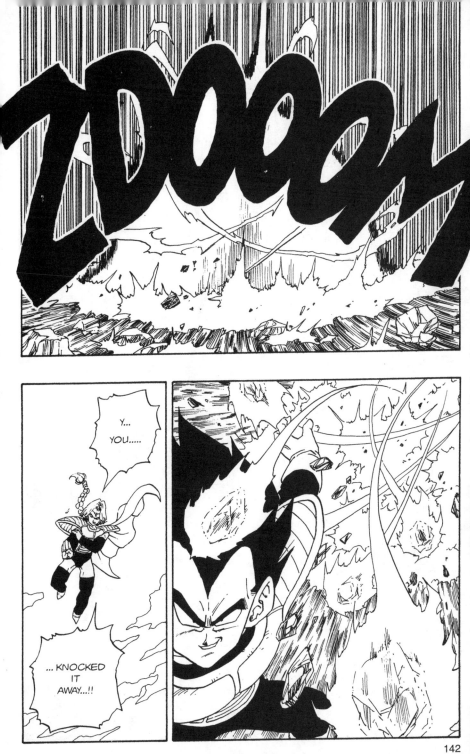

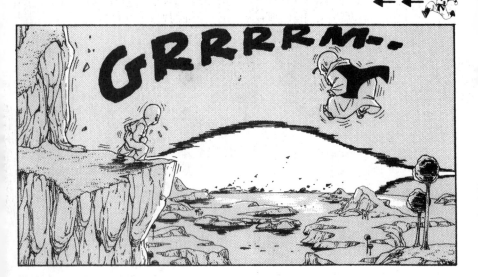

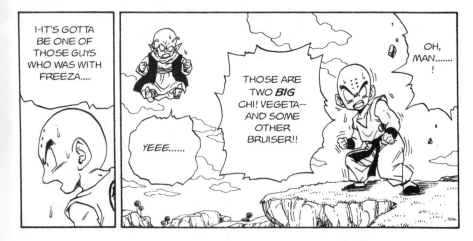

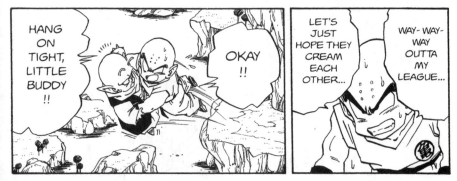

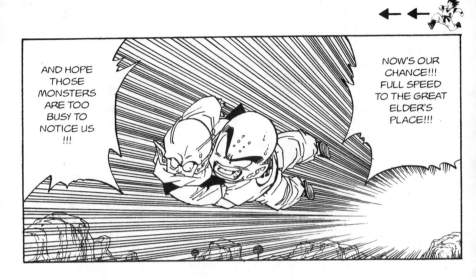

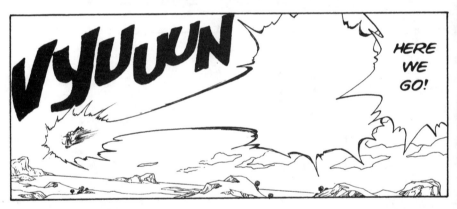

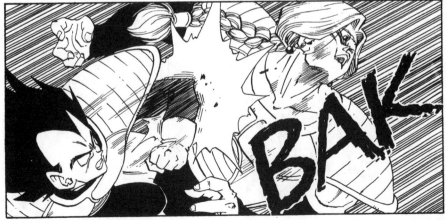

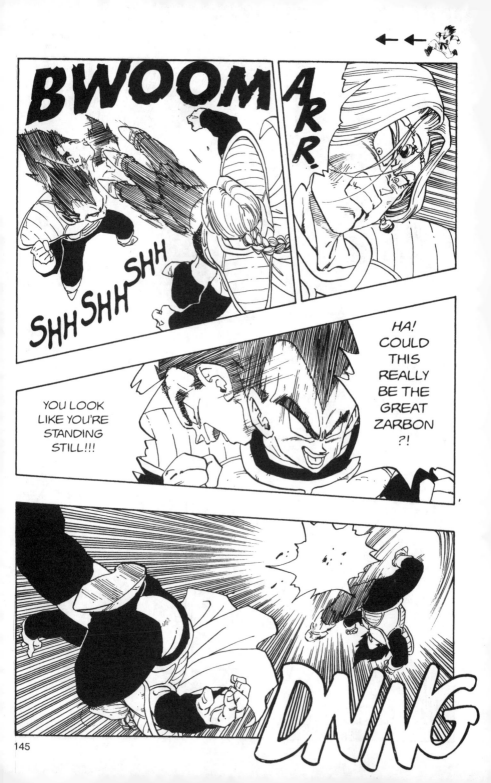

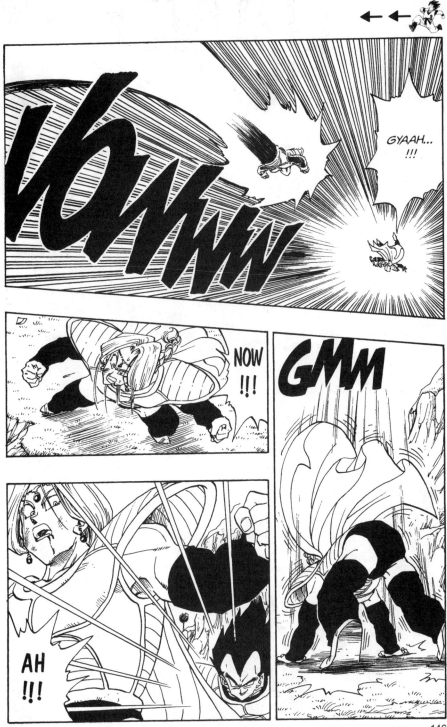

AND THAT'S AWAKENED THE POWER THAT'S LAIN *DORMANT* IN ME FOR YEARS....

YOU'VE HIT ME *HARD*, VEGETA...

HAH!

I HAVEN'T BROKEN A SWEAT, ZARBON!!

HUHH... HUHH... HEH HEH...

NEXT: *Zarbon's Surprise!*

DBZ:69 • Zarbon's True Power

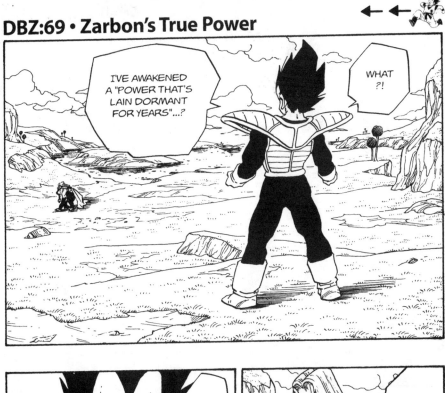

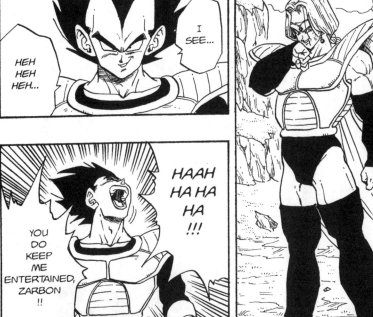

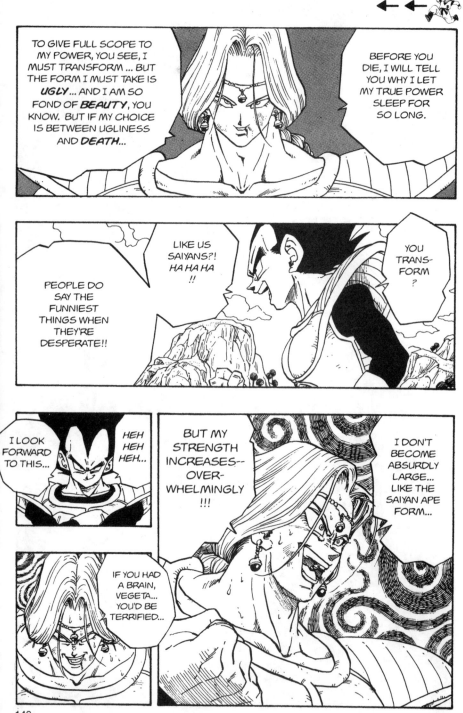

149

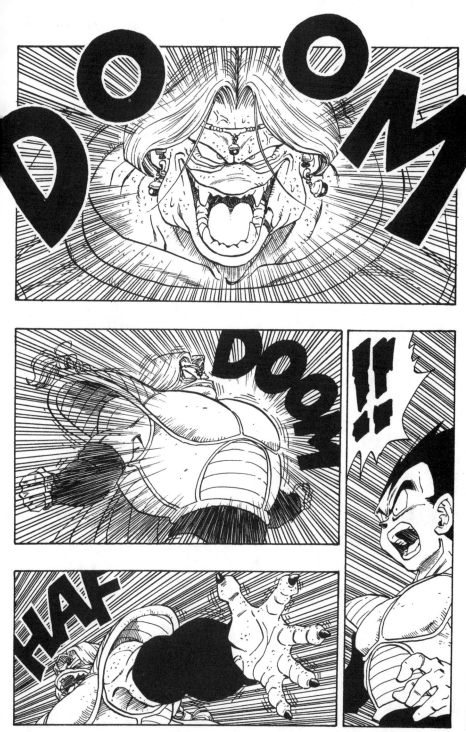

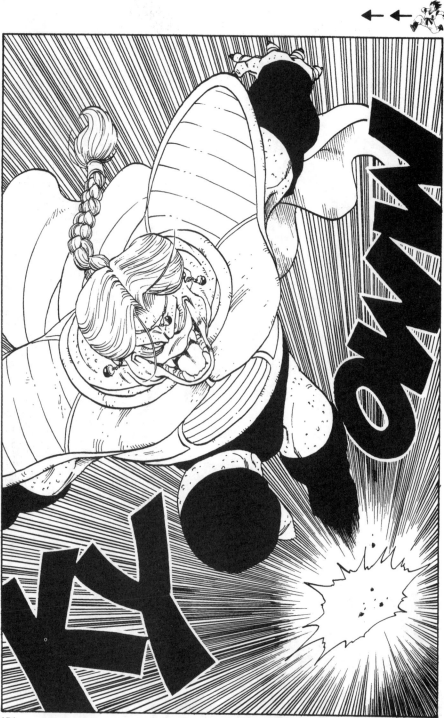

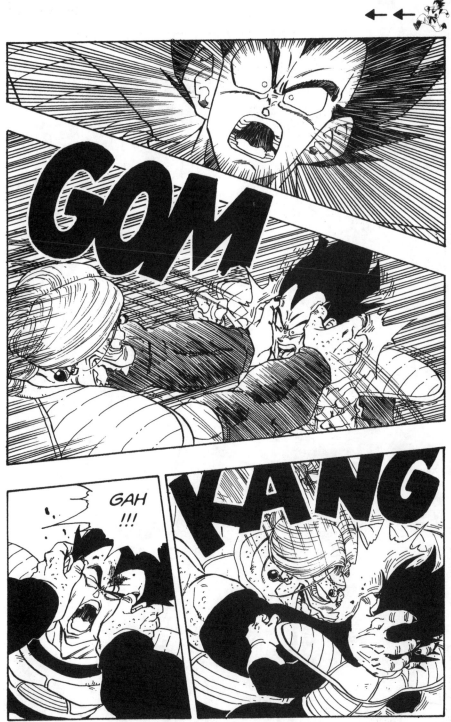

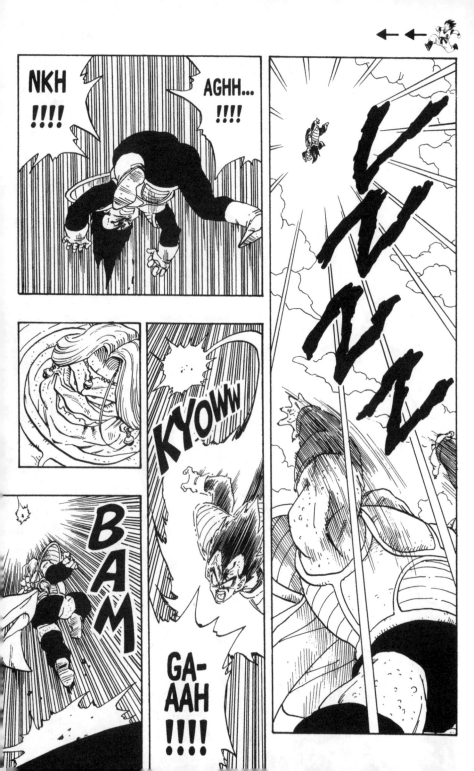

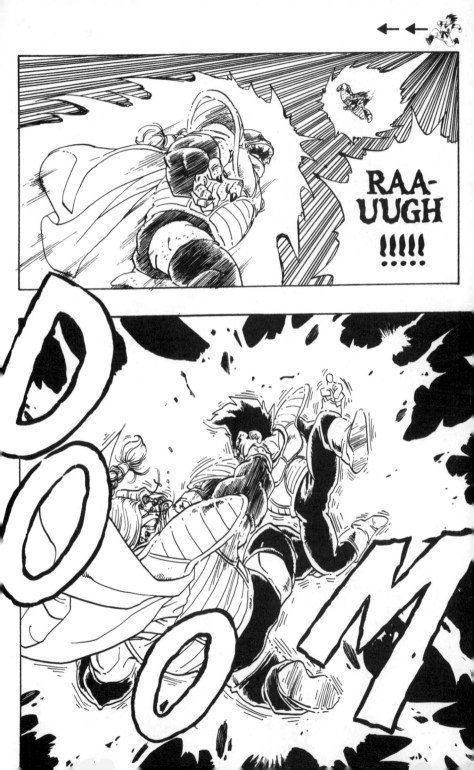

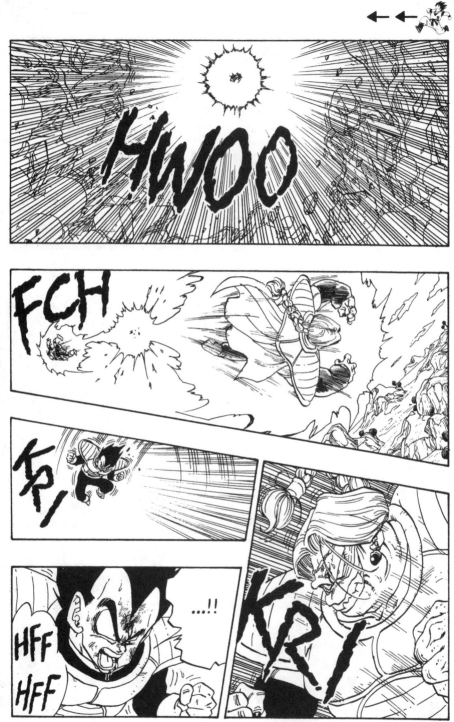

WH-WH-WHAT **IS** THIS... ?!!!

LET ME TELL YOU SOMETHING ELSE TO PONDER IN YOUR AFTERLIFE...

...UHH...!

I TOLD YOU, VEGETA...YOU HAVE ONLY YOURSELF TO BLAME FOR BEING SURPRISED...!

MASTER FREEZA HAS TOLD ME THAT HE, TOO, TRANSFORMS!

WHAT...?!

A TERRIBLE MISJUDGMENT, WASN'T IT? YOU'VE VASTLY IMPROVED YOUR SKILL, BUT YOUR ARROGANCE IS EVEN WORSE!

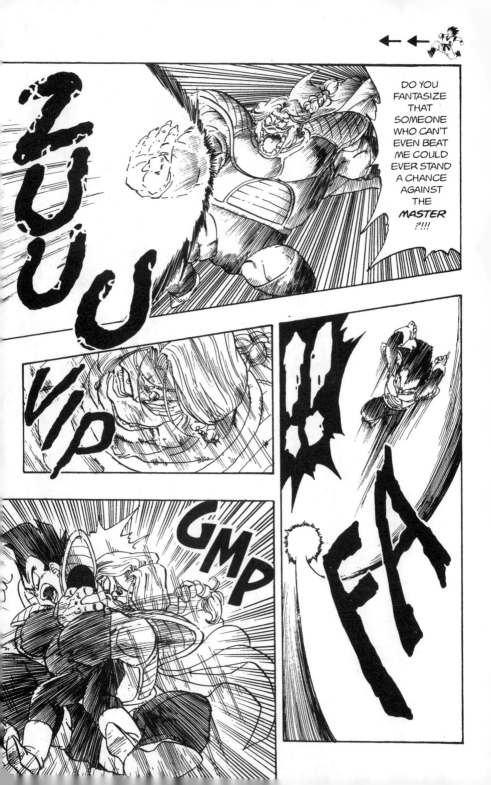

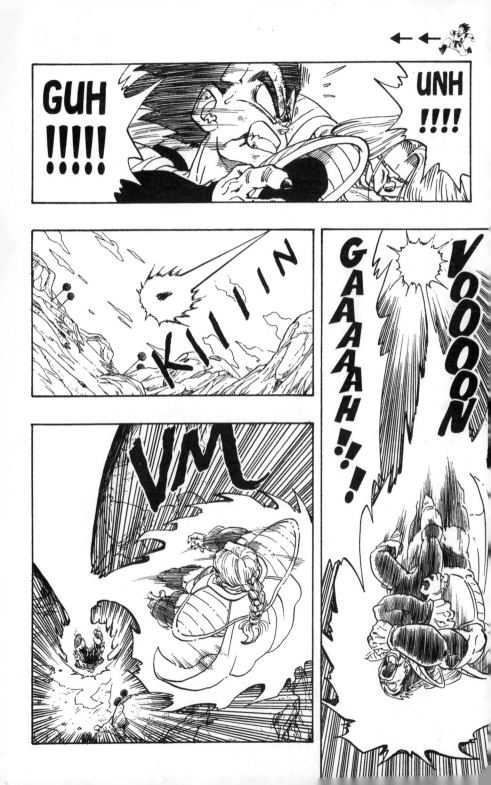

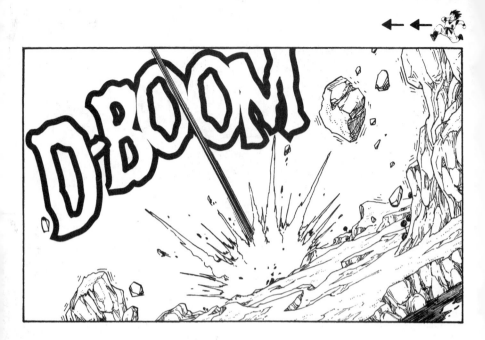

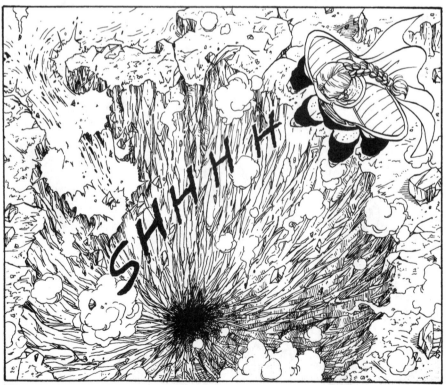

RRRBLE

GLUB

GLUB

HEH... BUT HOW LONG CAN EVEN HE LIE STILL IN WATER WITHOUT DROWNING?

...

IS HE DEAD...?

HE'S NOT SHOWING HIMSELF...

HEH... AND EVEN IF HE DID SURVIVE...

PF

I'M SURE HE WON'T WANT ANOTHER PIECE OF ME, NOW THAT HE'S SEEN MY FULL POWER!

VEGETA'S TOUGH... AND TREACH-EROUS...

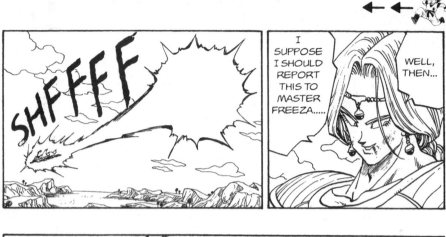

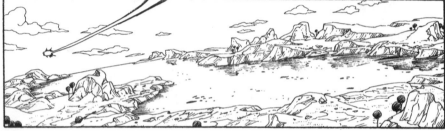

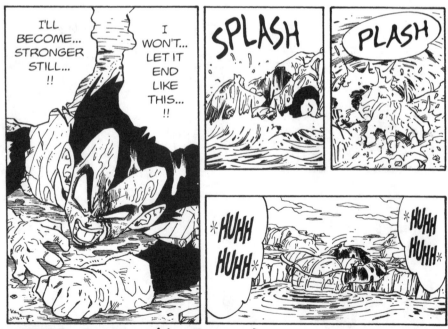

NEXT: *Captured by Freeza!*

DBZ:70 • The Great Elder's House

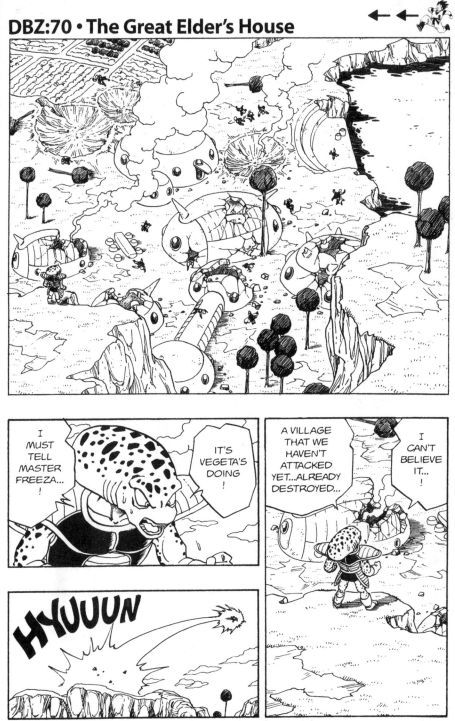

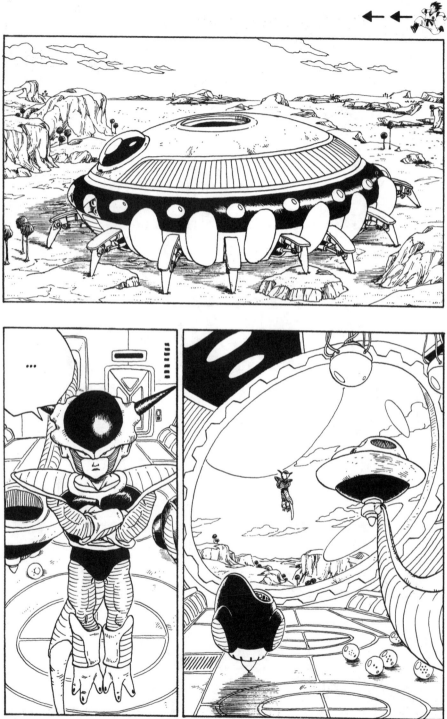

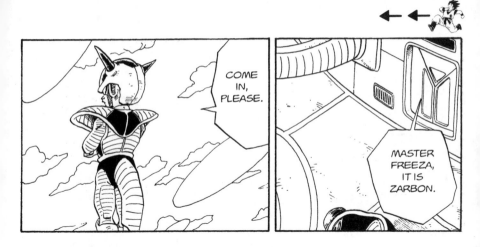

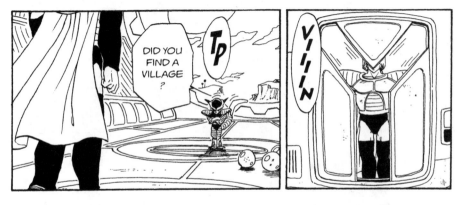

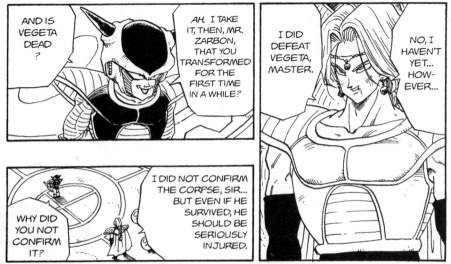

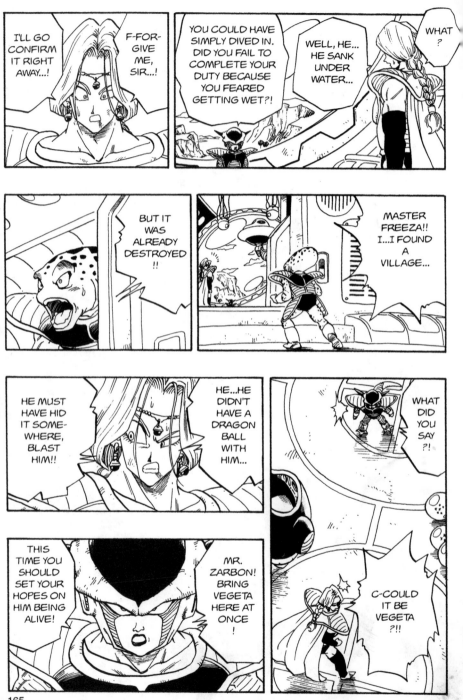

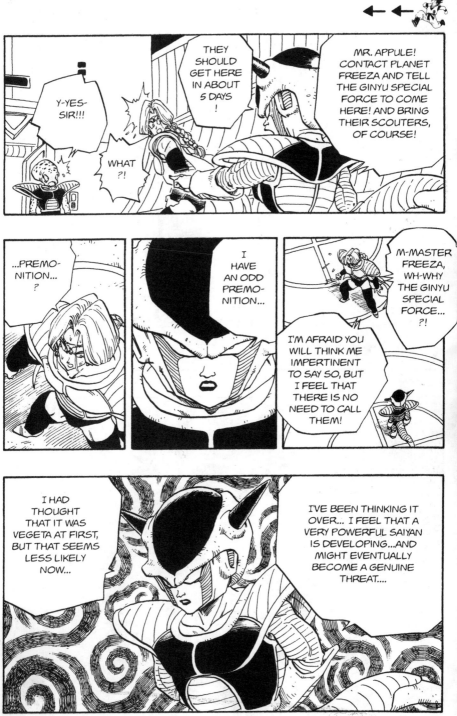

166

YOU WOULD DO BETTER SIMPLY TO BRING VEGETA TO ME.....

Y-YES-SIR!!

ARE YOU SAYING THAT I AM GIVEN TO FANTASIES, MR. ZARBON?

BESIDES VEGETA, THE ONLY SAIYANS ARE WHAT'S-HIS-NAME ON THAT PLANET CALLED EARTH...AND HIS SON...

AND THEIR BATTLE STRENGTHS ARE MUCH WEAKER THAN VEGETA'S...!

BUT SIR, HOW LIKELY COULD THAT BE...?

FYOOOO

IT DOES SEEM ABSURD THAT ONE COULD EVER BE A MATCH FOR ME, OF COURSE...BUT I MUST THINK OF THE FUTURE AND NIP THE BUD WHILE I CAN...

THE SAIYANS DO INDEED SEEM TO HAVE BOTTOMLESS COMBAT ABILITIES... THEY IMPROVE GREATLY EVERY TIME THEY SURVIVE A BATTLE...

IT WOULD BE MORE THAN A NUISANCE IF THEY WERE TO BECOME SUPER SAIYANS...

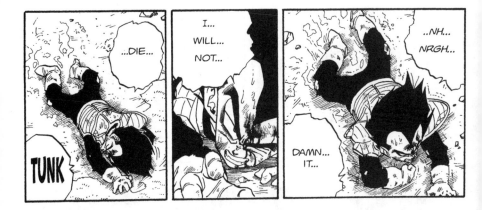

...DIE...

TUNK

I...
WILL...
NOT...

..NH...
NRGH...

DAMN...
IT...

BY THE
GODS...
!

TMP

EH
?!

KIIIII—N

THE
GINYU
SPECIAL
FORCE...

WE'LL GIVE THE LUCKY FOOL MEDICAL TREATMENT...SO THAT WE CAN MAKE HIM CONFESS WHERE HE HID THE DRAGON BALL!

AFTER THAT... WELL, LET'S HOPE DEATH HAS ANOTHER TURN!

AS IT TURNS OUT, THAT'S A BLESSING...

HE WAS ALIVE! WHAT DOES IT TAKE?!

VMM

HUF

GOKU TRAINS AND TRAINS, WITHOUT SLEEP OR REST...

HUF

WITH THREE SUNS IN ITS SKY, NAMEK NEVER KNOWS DARKNESS. AS THE SUNS WHEEL, ONE ENDLESS DAY BECOMING ANOTHER...

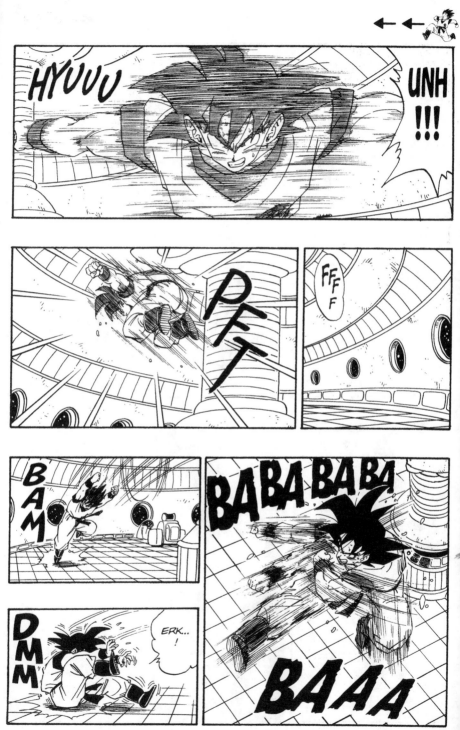

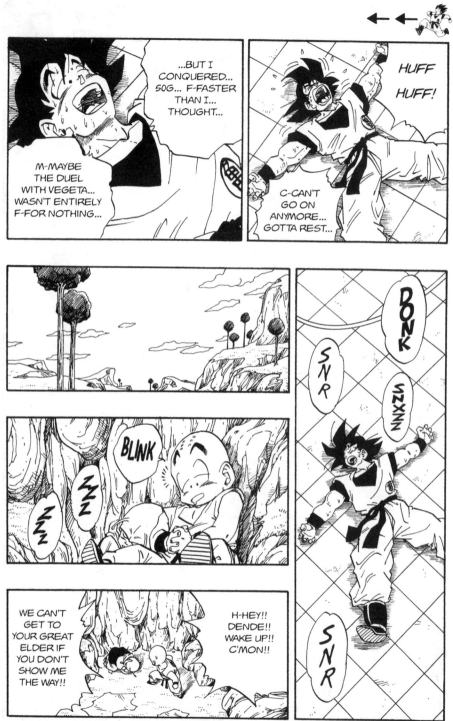

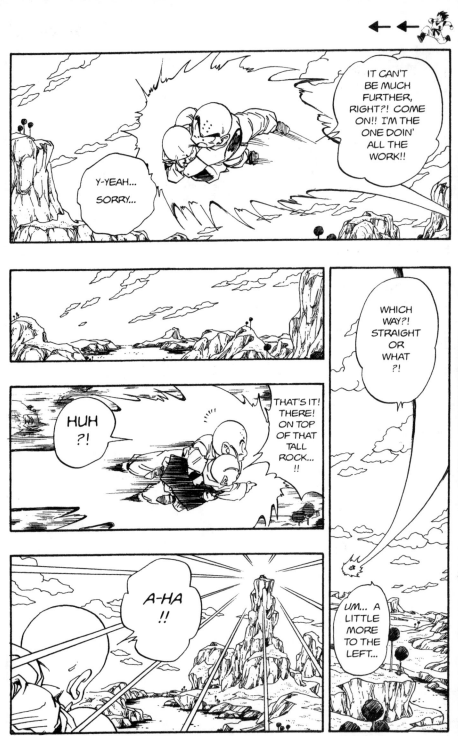

172

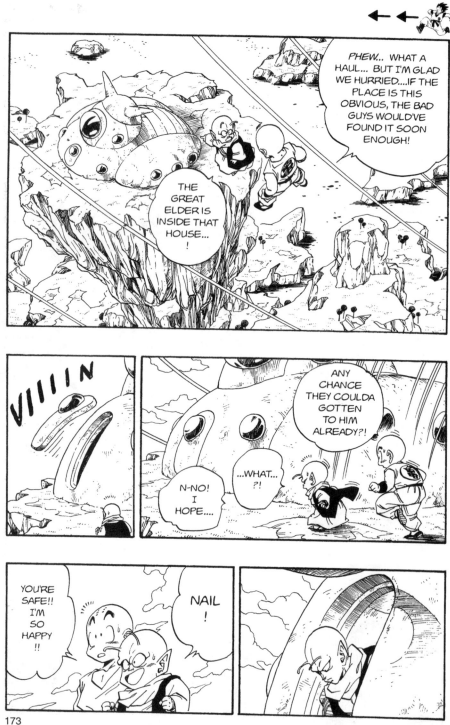

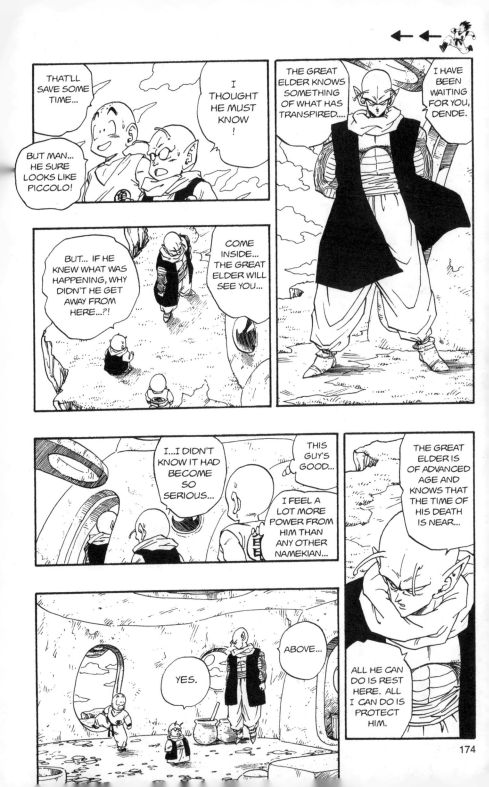

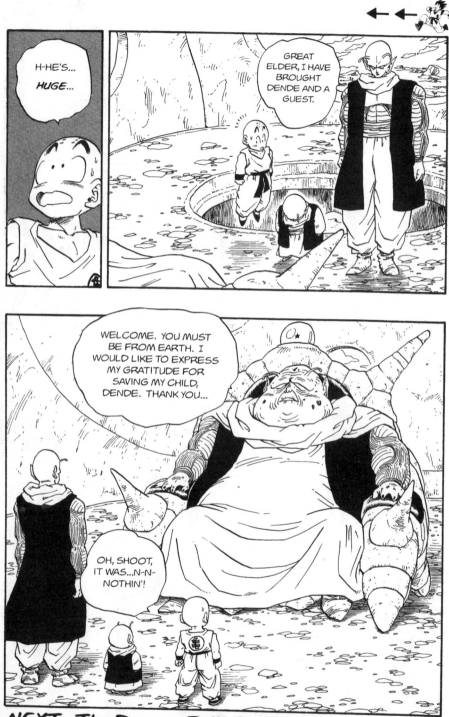

NEXT: *The Dragon Balls Change Hands!*

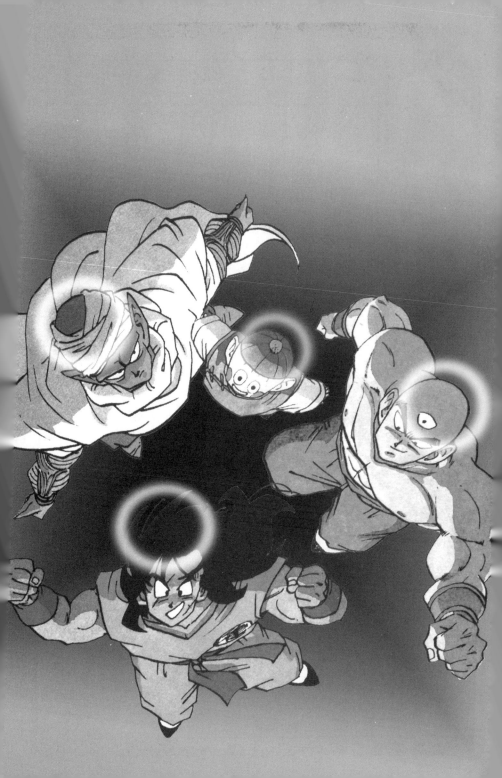

TITLE PAGE GALLERY

DBZ:60 • Ten Seconds of Death

WILL THEY EVER RETURN TO LIFE?

Here are the chapter title pages which were used when **Dragon Ball Z Vol. 6** was originally published in Japan in **Shônen Jump** magazine. Some were previously published in Viz's **Dragon Ball Z** monthly comic series; some have never before been seen in America!

FREEZA BETRAYS THE NAMEKIANS!!!

DBZ:61 • Son Gohan Snaps!

COMPARE THIS TITLE IMAGE TO THE FACING PAGE...

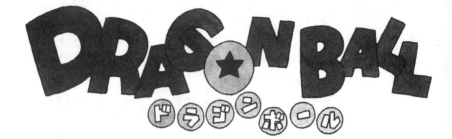

RUN FOR YOUR LIVES, GOHAN AND KURIRIN!

DBZ:62 • Death in Flight

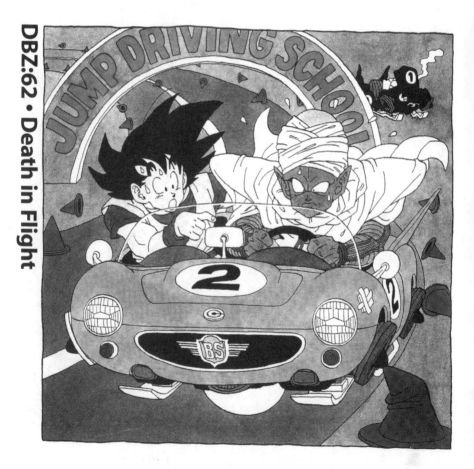

DRAGON BALL

WHATEVER DOESN'T KILL HIM...
MAKES HIM STRONGER!

DBZ : 63 • Vegeta vs. Dodoria

Akira Toriyama
BIRD 鳥山明 STUDIO

DRAGON BALL

TRAIN, GOKU! YOU CAN'T LET VEGETA BEAT YOU!

DBZ:64 • Hide and Seek

Akira Toriyama
鳥山明 BIRD STUDIO

DRAGON BALL

ALL BUT ONE...
IN THE CLUTCHES OF EVIL!

DBZ : 65 • The Sixth Dragon Ball

Akira Toriyama
鳥山明
BIRD STUDIO

DRAGON BALL

ドラゴンボール

WHO WILL GET IT???

Akira Toriyama

鳥山明
BIRD STUDIO

DBZ:66 • The Last Dragon Ball

DRAGON BALL

YOU WON'T LIKE ME WHEN I'M ANGRY...

DBZ:69 • Zarbon's True Power

ドラゴンボール

Akira Toriyama
BIRD 鳥山明 STUDIO

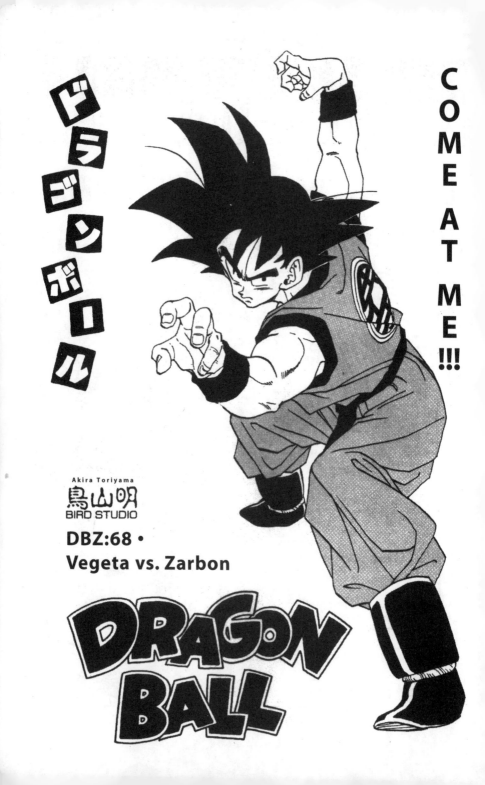

DRAGON BALL

UNTIL THE DAY THEY LIVE AGAIN...
THERE'S NOTHING TO DO BUT TRAIN!

DBZ:67 • The Four Dead Heroes

Akira Toriyama
BIRD 鳥山明 STUDIO

DRAGON BALL

WHO IS THE PROGENITOR OF THE NAMEKIANS?

DBZ:70 • The Great Elder's House

ドラゴンボール
Akira Toriyama
BIRD 鳥山明 STUDIO

Why do you love NO NEED FOR TENCHI!

It's the *greatest!* It's almost like a *shōjo* manga, with all those sparkly lights and zip-a-tone and big watery eyes!

Not to men-tion the *witty* writing and *sophis-ticated* romance... although I'm sure certain *space pirates* prefer the fight scenes...

I prefer the *comic relief* courtesy of certain *spoiled alien princesses!* I don't mind getting a few speed lines on me, if that's what you mean!

sigh... I like the letters and fan art...

I don't even show up in the anime! But in the *manga* I get revenge on my arch-rival Washu!

I like the catering!

Uhh...I was going to say I liked the science fiction ele-ments...

AVAILABLE NOW IN MONTHLY COMICS OR GRAPHIC NOVELS!
GRAPHIC NOVELS • 176-184 pages • $15.95 each

As seen on the Cartoon Network!

CALL OR GO ONLINE FOR COMIC SUBSCRIPTIONS
(800) 394-3042 • www.j-pop.com

VIZ COMICS

THE ART OF

MOBILE SUIT GUNDAM WING

A collection of killer art from the most popular show on the Cartoon Network!

MOBILE SUIT GUNDAM WING

BLIND TARGET

ON SALE NOW!

MARCH 2001

VIZ COMICS ™

©Sunrise/Sotsu Agency
©Hajime Yatate/Yoshiyuki Tomino/Sakura Asagi/Akemi Omode
First published in Japan by Gakken Co., Ltd.

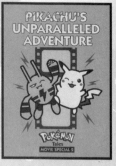
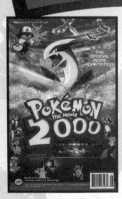
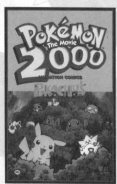
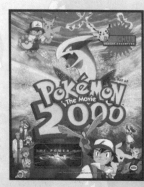
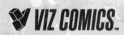
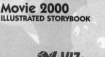

THE COMIC THAT STARTED IT ALL IS NOW AVAILABLE IN AMERICA!

DRAGONBALL

STORY AND ART BY AKIRA TORIYAMA

48 PAGES AN ISSUE

The amazing origin story of Son Goku is available in your local comics store! Find out the secret background of Piccolo, Kuririn, Tenshinhan, Kame-Sen'nin and more! Plus fan art, letters and more in each issue! Available in individual issues at your local comics store. Or subscribe and have it delivered to your door each month!

UNCUT AND UNCENSORED!

Online www.vizkids.com

RECOMMENDED AGES 3 AND UP